The Mantle of Mercy

Vincent DePaul

Leo Weismantel

THE
MANTLE
OF
MERCY

Translated by
ALBERT PAUL SCHIMBERG

THE BRUCE PUBLISHING COMPANY
MILWAUKEE

Translator's Note

IT IS a background of distressing blackness against which the author paints his portrait of St. Vincent de Paul. Gaume tells us: "During the seventeenth century, Hell continues the terrible battle begun in the previous century" (*Catechism of Perseverance*, Vol. III, p. 582). He speaks of the deluge of paganism which corrupted the minds and hearts of men, and of the "crowd of sects, daughters of the Renaissance and of Protestantism, come one after another to attack the Church, and to be broken into pieces against this immovable rock."

In contrast to the darkness of his times, how radiant the figure of our hero! His face is aglow with the tender light of divine compassion, there are about him the aura of heroism and the halo of holiness. And sharing in the effulgence are his associates in performing the spiritual and corporal works of mercy.

Beyond the frame within which the author chose to work, extends the acute play of lights and shadows. Bright against the gloom shine such figures as the gently wise St. Francis de Sales and St. Jane Frances de Chantal in France. In Italy, there were St. Angela de Merici of the Ursulines, the illustrious Jesuit,

Cardinal Bellarmine, and a man after the heart of the
peasant priest of Pouy, no matter how different from
him, the swashbuckling soldier and gambler who became St. Camillus de Lellis, first to make the Red
Cross an emblem of pitying help. And in Spain, there
was the glorious St. Teresa of Avila, indubitably one
of the greatest women of history. Across the seas
turbulent with the envies which gold and power beget,
the New World's first flower of sanctity blossomed in
the Peru of the Conquistadores, while in the snows of
New France sons of Old France made martyr trails.

As fiendish as the savages of Canada were the perse-
cutors of the Church in Great Britain and Ireland.
Before the century ended, Blessed Oliver Plunkett was
taken from his prison in Dublin to become the last in
the long line of martyrs at Tyburn Tree. To the exiles
from these lands and all others, the big heart of St.
Vincent de Paul went out in godlike pity. His charity
knew no boundaries, it spoke all tongues, it tran-
scended all differences. It was as universal as the
Church he loved so much, the Church her enemies
have martyred so often. And in a day when this is happening once again, it is well for us to consider this son
of hers whose heart was anguished because she was
shackled, but whom nothing could blind to her ancient
beauty and eternal youthfulness, and who was aflame
with the desire to help her children everywhere.

Writing of this epoch, Gaume declares that "against
all the efforts of Hell to destroy the work of redemp-

tion, God places the Church, but the Church fortified, defended by the great Doctors and the great
Saints; the Church become the mother of a hundred
and ten religious orders or congregations; the Church
shining with a vigor altogether new and extending her
conquests throughout the four quarters of the world"
(*Ibid.*).

Thus we see that in the seventeenth century (as before and since), despite the onslaughts of Hell, despite
her subjection by ruthlessly ambitious rulers and her
betrayal by apostate sons, the Church did not falter in
the fierce struggle, but continued her divine work
among men, and gave to all succeeding ages St. Vincent
de Paul and other tall and gallant spirits, to make
bright pages in her history and bear witness to her
deathlessness.

CONTENTS

Third Book: Good Deeds Without End

The Mantle of Mercy

Vincent gives his savings to a beggar.

Chapter I

THE PEASANT BOY OF GASCONY

THERE is a strange land in the southwestern part of France, between the Bay of Biscay and the Pyrenees. As the Alps do, but with harsher abruptness, the mountains rear their bulks like a vast chain to bar the way southward and call a halt to all that would go farther.

From rifted mountain valleys wild brooks dash downward, carrying stones and earth to the lowlands spread out before them. But this taxes their strength, so they let the heavy burden fall and run on, as though they had lost the way. Through the deposits they have made and with many troubled windings they seek a path westward to the great sea.

From the sea the booming surf hurls back upon the land the sand that the rivers have carried to the shore.

So this is a watery and a stony land. Beyond the dunes lie the swamps; and farther upwards, where the surface waters fail, is the heath.

The people who live there must depend upon this ungenerous soil. They are poor peasants, and often youthful unrest sends their boys forth on adventurous quests.

From the Bay of Biscay storms blow many days of the year. On old maps you can see how several puff-cheeked angel heads are set about this bay. They are the angels of the winds, who blow from all directions until the waves tower as high as houses and the ships dance on their crests, tossed about like leaves that fall from autumnal trees. God be with those who brave the high sea's dangers!

Inland, where the peasants dwell in their little houses built of stones, there are flocks of sheep and herds of swine, the swine in the low, marshy places, the sheep on the moorland. And stilts are used by those who watch the animals.

This strange land is called Gascony, the land of the ancient Vascones, a Pyrenean folk full of adventure in their dreams and in their speech. They are prone to boast and have much to tell, much to sing of wars and great captains.

Ever since ancient times, those coming from inner Europe have stormed across the mountainous barrier of Gascony, for beyond lay rich lands. The Ostrogoths lost blood and life here and the ground sucked up the blood like dung. And then, behold, from the other side came the Saracens. From Africa by way of Spain they came, and their purpose was to strangle and murder the Christendom of Europe.

A Frankish army was led against the Saracens by a hero whose name was Charles Martel. He defeated them here, at Tours and at Poitiers.

Later the knights of Charlemagne charged through the rifted mountain valleys into the land of the Moors, and when they were returning home it happened; in the Vale of Rouncesvalles the treacherous Saracens from ambush shot Roland, the paladin, with their arrows.

And ever since then, on certain nights the shepherds of Gascony hear Roland's horn, Oliphant, with which he warned Charlemagne his king; and the sound of the horn is heard as far away as Paris.

One of the rivers that issue from the inland hills and flow northward in wide-sweeping curves, then bend southward and finally westward to the Biscayan gulf, is called the Adour. On this stream, near the cathedral city of Dax, there is a little village, the railway station of which is proud today to call itself the cradle of St. Vincent de Paul. Formerly the place was called Pouy. That was when people wrote the year 1581 on their letters.

At that time there lived at Pouy a peasant farmer named Jean de Paul. His small house stood in a moist lowland between tall poplars. There the heath began.

The house was like a stable into which only a few rooms had been built for the peasant family. It was broader than high, bare and poor. Jean de Paul had to wrestle with the hardships of life. He was a thin little man, and lame. Once in his boyhood, hurrying after his herd that was fleeing before a storm, one of his stilts caught between two stones and he was dashed to the ground. He had been a cripple since then and could never again do a man's full work. There helped him his wife, whose name was Bertrande de Moras, a goodhearted, motherly woman. Year in, year out she was her own servant and worked for those in the little home, her husband and their two children.

But now a third child came, a boy. They christened him Vincent. The mother, when she chose his name, thought of the martyred Vincent whose bones were in a precious reliquary near the altar of the cathedral in Dax. It was scarcely more than an hour's walk from their peasant hut to the magnificence of the cathedral and the treasured relics of the Saint who had died for Christ in ancient days and before whose shrine a lamp burned always.

Often the peasant woman, Bertrande de Moras, had walked to the cathedral to gather strength of soul. And so, in answer to her husband's question, she said she wished to call the baby Vincent. The father was a bit startled, was silent a moment, then said, thoughtfully: "Yes, yes!" And when he remained sunk in thought she asked him what he was thinking about.

In the soul of the peasant Jean de Paul a dream lay hidden. In him was unrest, but in the mother a deep serenity.

Yes, the boy would be called Vincent — but the father's thought was of a Vincent other than the martyr whose relics lay enshrined in the cathedral of Dax.

While Bertrande de Moras was conformed wholly to the will of God, lived for her children and her home and did good to all as much as possible, and in her daily devotion to duty completed and perfected herself, in Jean de Paul there was a restless soul. His mind wandered beyond the village, out into the wide world, and he found the earth full of inequalities and injustices; saw his own life beset with harsh privations; saw that many — he needed to go but an hour's journey to Dax to see some of them — lived in easy comfort, even in luxury.

There was strife in the world, too; endless bickering, and the people seemed to know no rest. Only in this secluded hamlet of Pouy was there tranquillity. Out there, as soon as the heath came to an end, were violence and murder, burning and warfare. And of this the peasant Jean de Paul had much to tell.

Once, about two hundred and fifty years before he lived, the world had fallen very low. The whole of Christendom, instead of being the people of God, seemed to have become a single big band of robbers who attacked their brothers no less than their enemies. They had even driven the Pope out of Rome and he had fled to Avignon in France, near to the land where Jean de Paul lived.

At that time there arose one called Vincent — Vincent Ferrer. Into his soul a seraph had entered, so that he spoke as with a tongue of fire. Wherever he appeared the people gathered in throngs. He lifted his hands heavenward and began to speak with power. Those about him were enkindled by the mere sight of him, even if they understood scarcely a word of what he said.

Then those who had quarreled and harbored hate toward each other until that hour, felt the ice of their hearts melt. They sank to their knees, wept, and in the presence of all the people confessed their sins.

Jews and Moors who came out of curiosity were swept into the stream of fate and changed. They did as the Christians did, fell upon their knees, and asked to be baptized.

At that time there were among the people a large number who had fallen away from the Church. They called themselves the Cathari; that is, the Pure Ones, because, so they asserted, they had purified themselves, kept themselves unsullied, while all others lived in sin. Those who remained faithful to the old religion called these innovators the Heretics; or the Albigenses, because so many of them lived in the town of Albi in southern France.

Now the Cathari rejected the Church and the Old Testament, refused to obey civil authorities, denied the resurrection of the body, and called servants of Satan all who believed in Hell. They tried to deride the faithful by saying that God needed no oven in which to roast the disobedient. Thus they scorned the Church and her doctrines and practices. So far did they carry their rage against all oaths, against war and the death penalty for crimes that they fell upon those who did not believe as they believed, made war upon them and killed them. And they taught, too, that the soul of man wanders through the world and that birth and death are nothing more than the transmigration of the soul from one body to another.

These heretics maintained also that it was a sin to kill an animal and eat its flesh. They only kept themselves pure in body and soul who ate naught but the products of the fields and the fruits of trees and plants.

The errors of the Cathari spread among the people like a plague. But where Vincent Ferrer appeared, even the Albigenses were converted and won back to the Church's Communion of Saints.

At this time the Emperor of the West called a council at Constance, and Vincent Ferrer the mighty preacher arose and taught that the Pope at Avignon and the Western Emperor must unite in the Name of Christ, so that peace could be restored to the world.

This did Vincent teach, and when he departed from a town the place was as if transformed. Many followed him, so that he and the immense numbers with him made a continual pilgrimage through southern France, over into Italy, on toward Constance.

It was this Vincent that Jean de Paul, the peasant of Pouy, had in mind when he gave his baby son the name Vincent; and he probably had in mind, too, that Vincent Ferrer, the Saint, would take this tiny namesake of his in hand and make him what he had been, a priest. For Jean de Paul, the lame one, had seen that in the city of Dax none lived so well and were held in such high honor as the clerics. They had rich benefices, so that things went well with them. And in addition, the people always brought them offerings, so that on days when he was utterly tired and discouraged, the peasant would say to himself in desperation: "Who has much, receives more; who has almost nothing, from him something is always taken!"

So he prayed to St. Vincent Ferrer to take charge of the young Vincent de Paul and lead him to Dax and into the circle of clerics, and see to it that his protégé received a generous benefice, one large enough so that Vincent could help his parents and his brothers and sisters when they became old.

Such were the thoughts of the peasant Jean de Paul of Pouy.

In truth, his needs grew no fewer, but increased. After Vincent, his wife bore him another son, their fourth one, whom they called Gayon; and then two girls, whom they gave the names Marie and Marie Claudienne.

Meanwhile the little Vincent had grown to be a sturdy lad able to herd the swine and sheep. He was as healthy and lively as his father had been and could already run so adroitly on his stilts that the father laughed and forgot what it was that had made him a cripple. Jean de Paul hurried as best he could after his young son on the stilts, encouraging the lad. But when the boy stumbled the father cried out to him to be careful lest the stones dash him to the earth.

The father told Vincent all he needed to know to watch the sheep and pigs, pointed out to him the treacherous places in the swamps of the lowlands and of the watery, stony ground. And often he sat beside the lad and spoke to him of Vincent Ferrer, of the Cathari, of pilgrimages, and of wars. And then phantasies welled up in the heart of the boy and dreams of adventure took possession of him.

However, there were many long hours during which young Vincent was alone with the animals. He walked about on his stilts and from the heath gazed far out into the wide world. When he looked westward, the wind from the Bay of Biscay came and played with his hair. Then he braced himself against the wind and this pleased him.

But sometimes, in the evening when the sun sank blood red, Vincent stared with amazement into the flaming West, at the holocaust of the elements.

Was the time returning in which Vincent Ferrer strode through the land?

To be sure, his father had told him that had happened two hundred and fifty years ago. But the lad did not understand and the past became very near and alive for him, and he knew nothing of today and nothing of tomorrow. When he gazed thus into the blood-colored West of sunset and then darkness swallowed up all things, he forgot the animals he was watching and the world became for him a land of adventurous dreams and of wars and terrible deeds.

In the northern heavens, before the sun sank into the sea that glowed like rubies, there appeared to him in awesome pictures the Angel of the Judgment. And the angel set the trumpet to his lips and Vincent heard how the angel blew the trumpet so that the whole earth shook.

At that time, when Vincent de Paul was a boy and guarded his father's sheep and swine, all of France was torn by a fierce civil war, as in the days of Vincent Ferrer. Teachers of new errors had appeared among the people and their teaching spread from place to place in the land.

Once, when the two were on a journey, his father had pointed out to Vincent the direction in which lay a lakeside city, far to the northwest, beyond the city of Avignon, where the Popes had lived. There a dour man had appeared one day and begun to preach. And this is what he preached:

It is not possible for man to be good and avoid evil. He is good or bad from the beginning; and this is the fate that hangs over him: Sin is inevitable and he is predestined to be the prey of Hell. But the elect know that they are saved and that they will be received into the realm of the blessed.

This teaching was so gloomy and so pitiless that those who clung to it began to deface and destroy all that was light and joyful in the churches, even the images of the saints; for the holy ones were witnesses against the new creed, having fought the good fight against sin, and won it.

Calvin, the father of this heresy, declared, too, that those who refused to submit to his teaching and cling to it steadfastly, ought to be bound and burned at the stake, or strangled.

The adherents of the new creed were called Huguenots. Many understood this word to be a corruption of the Swiss term *Üdgenoten* (*Eidgenossen*), those who took an oath. Others, however, asserted that it was derived from the name of a man, Hugues Huguenots, formerly a leader of the Catholics in a Swiss town, later a renegade in the ranks of the Calvinists.

Like a fire did this heresy spread among the French people and those who clung to the ancient faith and those who followed Calvin attacked each other. The Huguenots stormed the churches, tore the pictures from the walls and smashed them. The Catholics resisted, sought to save the sacred images, and after fighting over the pictures the two factions fell upon each other and perpetrated endless violence.

The King of France was on the side of the Catholics, but those who wished to destroy the power of the throne went over to the Huguenots, not for the sake of the new religion but the more effectively to oppose the King. Two great families contested for the throne. One, the Guises, came forward as Catholic champions; the other, that of Navarre, led the Huguenots.

Then assassination and death by poisoning took place not only among the burghers but in the very shadow of the throne. The factions made peace agreements occasionally, but treacherously, because the one hoped to lure the other into a trap.

This civil strife had been devastating France for some decades before Vincent de Paul saw the light of day in Pouy of Gascony.

From his father Vincent had heard much about the many bloody encounters. The father knew a song about these things, a song that sounded sinister when sung in the gloaming at day's end.

When the boy Vincent, standing on his stilts, gazed into the blood-red dying sun, it seemed to him he could hear this song. The wind carried it to him and it told of a deed of cruelty and horror.

Vincent knew that the men who had done this deed were still living. Then he would turn his face northward and stare out over the land upon which the shadows of night were falling, stare toward the city of Paris. His father had shown him in what direction it lay.

There in Paris lived the King of France, Henry of Navarre, and the Queen, Marguerite of Valois. Only a few years before, King Charles IX of France, to give peace to his realm, had endeavored to compose the quarrels of the Catholics and Huguenots. He had summoned the leader of the Huguenots, Henry of Navarre, and had said to him: "I wish to establish peace between

you and me, and as a pledge of this peace I will give
you to wife my sister, who is called Marguerite of
Valois."

They called Marguerite then, the royal young
woman, and she was beautiful beyond all telling.

It was proclaimed throughout the land that peace
had come. From all parts of France leaders of the
Huguenots came to Paris, to honor Henry of Navarre,
for it was rumored among the people that when the
present King died Henry of Navarre would take his
place on the throne.

Could there be a surer pledge of peace than this?

So the reconciled factions celebrated the marriage
with such pomp and gaiety as France had never seen
before.

Vincent de Paul, the shepherd boy and swineherd,
saw in his dreams all the royal pomp of this wedding.
A childlike, utterly nameless love for Marguerite the
Queen took possession of him. It seemed to him that
he was a page in her retinue and was filled with happiness when she turned and looked at him.

The song which Vincent had learned from his father
so praised the loveliness of this woman that Vincent
the boy could not help but love her.

But there came a shudder in the night; and the song
continued:

And when they celebrated the marriage in Paris —
it was on the 18th of August in the year 1572 — and
the city was filled with songs of reconciliation and with

jubilation over peace restored, the Queen Mother went stealthily to the chamber of the youthful King. She opposed the marriage, so she said to her royal son:

"In truth, the Huguenots hate you and they have made peace under pretense of this marriage only to murder you."

Then before the frightened eyes of the boyish King she painted a word picture of such horror and treachery that before dawn the King commanded that the leaders of the Huguenots, who had come to Paris for the marriage of Henry of Navarre and Marguerite of Valois, should be murdered, all in this one night.

That was the night between the 23rd and the 24th of August of the year 1572, and the guests, pleasantly tired from the wedding celebration, slept all unawares.

Then in the eerie light of half dawn the bells of Paris began to ring out and at once there was a shot in the street. This was the signal at which the armed men of the King, secretly distributed through the city during the night, broke into the houses which had been marked for them, invaded bedrooms, drew the terror-stricken sleepers from their beds and killed them.

A wild lament arose in the streets and the deed of horror spread from place to place in the land, even to the farthest borders of the King's realm.

This was in the night before the feast of the blessed martyr Bartholomew; and therefore the deed of terror was called the bloody wedding of St. Bartholomew's Day.

Even into the sleeping room of the hero, Henry of
Navarre, the armed men dared to burst, and into the
chamber of his bride, Marguerite of Valois, the King's
sister. They would have killed Henry, too, had he not
during the night abjured the creed of the Huguenots
and returned to the ancient faith of the Catholic
Church.

Of all this the song sang, and the boy Vincent knew
that there to the north lay the city of Paris. Now
Henry of Navarre sat on the throne of the kings at
Saint-Denis, in a sacred place, as his father had told
him; in an ancient cathedral in which Charlemagne,
the great Emperor of the West, had knelt. There
Henry of Navarre had sworn adherence to the old
religion, and Marguerite of Valois sat as Queen beside
him on the throne.

Would Vincent serve her one day?

If war came again, he would go forth like St. Vincent Ferrer of old, fare through the land and on a
banner he would bear the image of his Queen.

Thus the boy dreamed many times as darkness fell
upon the heath.

But then he would be flooded with terror. For the
old song of his father was full of frightening things.

When night had thus fallen many times, and the
darkness had begun to disturb the peasant lad, he
began to sing another song, one which his mother, the
good woman, had taught him. And the dread was banished, the dread that the father's song had caused to

flow into the boy's blood was driven out by the
mother's song:

> *Salve, Regina,*
> *mater misericordiae —*
> Hail to the Queen who reigns above,
> Mother of clemency and love,
> Hail, thou, our hope, life, sweetness; we,
> Eve's banished children, cry to thee.
>
> We from this wretched vale of tears
> Send sighs and groans unto thy ears;
> Oh, then, sweet Advocate, bestow
> A pitying look on us below.

Chapter II

THE STILT BOY GOES TO SCHOOL

AS OFTEN as Vincent thought of Queen Marguerite and of the city of Paris and the pomp and glory of the royal court, he became feverish with anxious phantasies that passed over his soul as dark clouds pass across the sky.

But when he thought of the other Queen, she about whom his mother had taught him her song and to whom he sang the *Salve, Regina,* then he became happily tired as a child and was filled with a yearning to rest in the lap of this mother and go to sleep against her breast. It was his own bodily mother who took him to herself in such moments.

At such times Vincent felt an immense pity for the world, and he wished to wander through the land. Not, however, like a firebrand, like St. Vincent Ferrer, but quietly, secretly, so that none would see him. He wished to go to the poor and sick and do deeds of kindness for them.

Vincent was twelve years old when, conning such thoughts in his mind, he drove his father's donkey to the mill to get a sack of flour. On the homeward way he was roused from his dreams with a start when he

19

heard a voice cry out. By the roadside he saw a miserable old woman, who began to complain loudly as soon as she saw the boy and the flour bag on the animal's back. "Oh, how God in Heaven gives sackfuls of flour to the rich, so they can bake bread and cake, while I have not even a handful of flour with which to fill the hungry mouths of my children!"

The old woman was exceedingly thin, wasted by hunger and worry.

The boy was overwhelmed by a flood of pity. He halted the donkey, called to the woman to help him take the flour off the donkey's back. Then he opened the bag, bade the woman spread her apron and into it he spilled so much of the flour that the woman was speechless with amazement. But Vincent shouted to her gaily to help him put the sack back on the donkey, then he resumed his homeward journey with a cheerful heart.

However, when his father's hut loomed before him and the other children came running to meet him, the boy was deeply troubled, expecting his father to punish him and his mother to scold. For even if he had brought a full sack of flour from the mill, how many were the hungry mouths in the little house, how long would the sackful have to nourish all of them!

Jean de Paul came toward his son and gazed wonderingly at the half-empty bag on the donkey's back, and was about to denounce the miller for having sent only half a sackful, when Vincent began to make his stumbling confession.

For a moment the father stood staring. He would have wished most of all to have walked to the bench near the house and sat himself down, so full of care was he.

Then the mother came. What had happened? She looked about inquiringly. The little brothers and sisters, who knew that something extraordinary was afoot, stood silently by.

But the father only grumbled. What could he do? He did not punish Vincent. He led the donkey with the half-empty sack into the farmyard.

Thereupon the boy sprang after him and threw his arms around his father's neck, then hurried back to his mother and embraced her.

Only occasionally, at the sacred seasons of the year, the boy Vincent received a few small coins. These he saved, cherishing them like a precious treasure. Already he had thirty sous, approximately sixty cents in our present money. He took the cherished coins with him when he set out one day for the city to Dax, to buy something he had for months been longing to possess.

As he hurried along, where the lane from the paternal farm joined the highway, the lad almost ran into a beggar. The man shrank back, startled, and the boy was scared almost out of his wits. The beggar said: "Can't you see how hard it is for me to get on?"

Again Vincent was filled with a vast pity. He drew from his pocket the fist that clutched the precious savings, hurried to the beggar and put the thirty sous into his hands. The man blinked at him in utter astonishment and tears welled up in his eyes. The tears, however, frightened Vincent more than had the angry words. He fled homeward to his sheep and swine grazing on the moor and in the lowland swamp.

After a little while his mother heard him singing *Salve, Regina.*

So Vincent came to be fourteen years old. It was the year 1595. The father gave thought anew to his ambitious plan for the boy. To advance it he must take the lad to Dax. He put on his best clothes, took Vincent by the hand and led him forth.

The boy acquiesced, but he was troubled. He felt that this was no ordinary journey to the city and he let himself be led like a child. However, when they had left the countryside behind and reached the first houses of Dax, Vincent began to feel ashamed. He sought to withdraw his hand from that of his father, looked at his parent's bony, limping figure and compared it with those of the men who passed by in city clothes that were so elegant in his peasant eyes.

How poor his father looked, even in his Sunday coat! And he was crippled! It seemed to Vincent that they must look like two beggars in the street.

Thus they came to the Franciscan monastery, where the friars lodged a number of boys who attended a school elsewhere in the city. And Vincent stood by while his father conferred with the Guardian of the monastery regarding fees. The lad would gladly have gone away again, at once, because of the deep trouble he saw in his father's face when the friar told him how much he would have to pay. But finally Jean de Paul made up his mind. The boy would stay. How else could the goal be reached?

Yes, Vincent was to be a cleric, and Jean de Paul began to admonish him to study day and night, not to spare himself, remembering how those at home would deny themselves to keep him at school in the city.

There was no other way to prepare the son for the benefice which would later take care of the whole family.

The father seemed not at all abashed at voicing his expectations openly before the friars, and more than once shame brought tears to Vincent's eyes.

However, when the shabby, lame peasant farmer had gone, one of the Brothers took Vincent aside, spoke kindly to him, gave him books, showed him his place in the study room, and told him that if he studied diligently he would find that the time would pass for him and his family more quickly than he now imagined.

The next day Vincent went with the other boys to the school in Dax and the peasant's son from Pouy began to acquire what his teachers set before him.

He applied himself wholeheartedly, though all was strange to him and without appeal. He was filled with a single desire, to master the courses as soon as possible. It was a torture for him to know that his father, because of whose poverty he himself had been filled with shame, and his mother and his brothers and sisters, suffered privation on his account.

He allowed himself scarcely a moment of play with the other lads.

The Franciscans noticed this. Not long afterwards there came to the monastery a man of prominence whom the people called Monsieur de Comet, a counselor-at-law of the court in Dax and held in high esteem in the city. He was the father of a number of sons whom he wished to send to the school, but the lads did not care at all about books and studies. For this reason the proud and prominent Monsieur de Comet came to the monastery to find an older student, one at once needy and capable, whom he would take into his rich home to induce his sons to study and supervise them at their books.

Now it was true that Vincent, the peasant's son, had been at the school a few weeks only, but the friars had observed how more than any other student he helped those of his own age at their lessons, how he excelled the others in ability, and though himself a student seemed at the same time a teacher of his classmates.

So it came to pass that the Franciscans could recommend to Monsieur de Comet none more heartily than the peasant lad Vincent from Pouy, and the counselor took him into his home.

Vincent was overjoyed at the turn of events, for often in those days of utter loneliness and of worry about his loved ones at home, he had sung the *Salve, Regina* secretly in the night, with the petition to his heavenly Mother to help him realize his father's hopes. Therefore he believed that none but Mary, his Queen and Mother, had brought this about, and he gave himself with all diligence not only to his own studies but also to the instruction of the boys in his charge. And Monsieur de Comet came to hold him in deep affection, patted him on the shoulder at times, and promised to help him.

When Vincent had been at the school in Dax and in the home of Monsieur de Comet somewhat more than a year, the counselor-at-law called the tutor to him one day and announced that Bishop Salvat Deharse of Tarbes would arrive shortly in the near-by village of Bidache. Vincent was to make himself ready to take a letter to the prelate when he reached Bidache from Bayonne, a letter of greeting and recommendation from Monsieur de Comet, the lawyer.

But in the letter Monsieur de Comet wrote that the bearer was a student of the school at Dax, a diligent, worthy youth. The lawyer believed that, though only 15 years of age, Vincent de Paul was ready for and deserved to receive from the Bishop's hands the tonsure and the four minor orders.

When Vincent heard this he could scarcely believe that such good fortune had come to him. He remembered that his father had told him how in addition to ability, faithful attention to duty, and all the qualities that help a man advance, rich and influential friends were needed. Therefore Jean de Paul had admonished his son, even before he took him to Dax, not only to study with zeal but also to be on the alert to acquire powerful patrons.

Well, so Vincent went forth, with a prayer on his lips, on the day Monsieur de Comet had designated and at Bidache he received the tonsure and the four minor orders. This took place on the 20th of December in the year of our Lord, 1596.

Now that he had completed his first studies, Vincent had to consider his university courses. Monsieur de Comet, his paternal friend, told him the possibilities: Paris, Bordeaux, Toulouse.

"Later," said the lawyer, "it must be Paris, for there Jacob's ladder touches the earth. Whoever wishes to advance cannot neglect Paris. But the city is also a den of wild beasts. Perhaps it were not well to send you there now. Living costs more in Paris, too, and your father is poor. So I advise you to go to Toulouse. I have influential friends there who will help you."

Vincent followed this counsel. But before setting out for Toulouse he hurried to Pouy, to the home of his parents, who embraced him with much joy. The father, who saw his goal appreciably nearer, decided to take a pair of oxen to the market, though he could ill afford to do so, and give the proceeds to his son when he left for the university.

Toulouse lies on the River Garonne, on a highway that leads from the Mediterranean Sea but also from the Atlantic Ocean and the Bay of Biscay to Bordeaux, where the Garonne empties into the sea, and there is a great port busy with shipping.

To this city came Vincent, armed with the letters from Monsieur de Comet and the price of his father's oxen. He was from the first determined not only to pursue his studies with all zeal but to save all he could of his father's money and make the best possible use of the letters. He wished to do as he had done in Dax, teach the sons of a wealthy man. Making inquiries, he was told that about five hours' walk from Toulouse was a hamlet called Buzet, and from there a number of youths came to the university. Because, like Vincent, they had small means they found it less expensive to live at Buzet and helped each other, making periodical trips to Toulouse to sit at the feet of the renowned teachers of the university.

Vincent went to Buzet at once and managed to rent a number of rooms in a house and there board and lodge a group of students. Thus with his father's ox money he established a little lodging house, or pension, and took charge of the sons of more prosperous parents.

The reputation of the capable young scholar spread

in the city, and noblemen of ancient lineage and famous names selected Vincent as mentor for their sons. In this way he was soon able to transfer his work to Toulouse.

Then, at 17 years of age, Vincent de Paul received the order of subdeacon, and three years later he was ordained deacon. Finally, on the 23rd of September, in the year 1600, and not yet 20 years old, he was raised to the holy priesthood.

In the meantime something had happened that confirmed his resolution to keep in the path he had been treading. Shortly after he had removed to Toulouse, his father, worn out by the hardships and worries of life, had died in the little house at Pouy. The old man left a will in which he admonished his widow and sons and daughters to spare themselves no sacrifice necessary to enable Vincent to become a priest. Until this was accomplished they ought not to complain of any privation, for afterwards Vincent would be able to repay them, his benefice would rescue them all from want.

This matter of a benefice had been like an obsession in the mind of poor old Jean de Paul. He had endured so much that he could imagine nothing more desirable than to be once and for all spared any further trouble, to gain security through his son's ecclesiastical living.

But when Vincent was called to his father's bier and from his mother heard of the last will and testament, he took his mother's hands in his and said to her:

"Never will I consent to this, that you here at home suffer privation on my account!"

He returned to Toulouse and worked day and night at his studies and to earn his daily bread.

Then came the day on which he was to offer up the Holy Sacrifice of the Mass for the first time.

It seemed to come upon him suddenly, this great day. True, he had taken each preceding step fully conscious of what it led to, but now when the young priest was close to the sublime goal, he realized completely for the first time that this was not a benefice, not a common meal, but the Supper of the Lord, the Bread of Angels.

And his mouth was about to speak the words over the host and cause the wonderful transformation, the changing of this bread in his trembling hands into the Body of Jesus Christ, the Son of God!

Thereupon he was seized by a nameless dread and awe. While the others ordained with him celebrated their first Masses in the festive circles of their families and friends, Vincent fled like a thief. Accompanied only by another priest, he hurried through the night from Toulouse to Buzet, where on a wooded height there was a little chapel.

To this chapel he had often gone in hours of discouragement and loneliness. How many times had he experienced consolation there in the old song of his mother, *Salve, Regina!*

It was nearly morning when they reached the

humble sanctuary. Vincent threw himself upon his knees in front of the sacred place. He prayed a long time, for he dared not enter. He felt that angels, mighty cherubim, surrounded the chapel, and if he opened the door and walked up the short aisle, the cherubim would stand to the right and to the left from entrance to altar.

Trembling, he arose when the other priest admonished him, and put off his mantle. As in a dream, it seemed to him, his friend helped him don the sacred vestments. And when the chalice was placed in his hands he went up to the altar.

Thus he began to celebrate for the first time the mystic Sacrifice with which the Son of God went to His bitter suffering and death and in which He gave Himself as Bread to men, for their salvation and the salvation of the world.

Once again, before the Consecration, the young priest was overwhelmed by a great fear. His body and his soul trembled when he spoke the mighty words. And in the moment in which he knew that now he no longer held in his hands the common bread but the true Body of God's Son, then it was to him as though the earth shook.

Why did men out in the world run after benefices, after riches which the moths consume, and forget the Bread of Life, which makes men good, welds them together as brothers, brings peace to the earth?

Then, before his own Communion, he thought of

them all — his poor father who because of a benefice had set his son in this path. Now his son held the benefice in his hands. Perhaps Jean de Paul was still suffering in Purgatory. And in spirit Vincent broke the Bread and placed a piece between the lips of his father, whose soul he saw with his mind's eye.

And in like manner he gave his mother Holy Communion, and then his brothers and sisters, and he called them by name, one after the other; and then his paternal patron, Monsieur de Comet. And all at once he thought, he knew not how, of that horrible night of the bloody wedding of St. Bartholomew's Day. Would the king come, too, Henry IV of France? Were not all of them coming, in a vast ghostly procession, the Cathari, the Huguenots, the Catholics — all of them, all who had been bitter enemies, had murdered each other; and all who now lived with hate in their hearts?

He believed that he had been given to see all this as in a vision. A year ago Henry of Navarre had put away his wife, Marguerite of Valois, and the marriage had been declared null and void. But in spirit the young priest placed pieces of the Host between their lips, as they knelt before him, so that they might partake of the Lord.

Thus, in spirit, he divided the Host, so that from his hands all received the Body of the Lord, the Bread of Salvation, the Bread of Judgment — for they ate the Lord — and all ate of Him and He remained unconsumed, the infinite Food, the divine Nourishment of unnumbered generations.

When they were returning to Toulouse, Vincent stopped to look back toward Buzet and the mysterious, secluded chapel on the wooded height. Then he heard about him the gossip and the laughter of promenaders — and the world of wonders vanished, he saw himself back in the realm of workaday facts, of sin and vice and hate and poverty.

What was he to do now? Yes, what was he to do?

He resolved to go to Dax, and so after visiting his mother and brothers and sisters at Pouy, he proceeded to the cathedral city and presented himself to the Bishop of Dax, to receive an appointment. The prelate received him with much friendliness and gave him the parish of Tilh, adding with a smile that it was one of the best parishes in the diocese, with a living such as few of them yielded. However, an unworthy priest whom the Bishop had deposed was still there. Vincent was to get his official papers at the diocesan chancery, go to Tilh and demand the benefice. If the deposed priest refused to leave, because he did not wish to lose the living, no matter that he had performed his priestly duties very badly or not at all — then Vincent was to appeal to the secular court. For in those days it was customary for churchly offices, those of Bishop and Archbishop even, to be filled at the behest of the King and his subordinates.

The secular officials did not hesitate to drive

bargains very often in the matter of benefices, granting them to those who guaranteed the highest commissions.

So Monsieur Vincent (as he was to be called henceforth) went to Tilh. But when he met the old priest there and presented his credentials, the deposed pastor began at once to quarrel with him and to let loose a flood of maledictions. Vincent left the house. Standing out in a field, he asked himself whether he ought to have recourse to the secular court and contend with the old priest for the benefice. Was not something infinitely more precious, the holy priesthood, his beyond all doubt, subject to no court, above all quarrels?

He left the other in possession of the worldly goods and began a pilgrimage to Rome, to pray at the tombs of Peter and Paul, the Princes of the Apostles, and ask the benediction of the Pope himself on his priestly work.

Quietly, almost secretly, Monsieur Vincent came back to Toulouse upon returning from his Roman pilgrimage. He had his little lodging house there still, also a small place where he instructed boys, and these he continued to manage. They gave him his daily bread. He wished also to make further studies at the university, to win a bachelor's degree and the right to expound the sentences of the philosophers.

In this way he lived until 1604. Not always had things been easy. He had been compelled to go into debt.

Then, in the autumn of 1605, when Vincent was 24
years old, he was summoned to the residence of the
Duke d'Epernon. This nobleman was the uncle of two
young students in Vincent's charge. He had met the
young priest repeatedly, had heard of his needy condition and was resolved to help him. Vincent was excited
when he returned from visiting the Duke, and prepared at once for a hasty journey. No one knew what
had happened. Some whispered. Perhaps the boys, the
nephews of the Duke, had gossiped about their uncle
having obtained a bishopric for Monsieur Vincent.

There must have been something extraordinary
about the matter, for Vincent was agitated and those
who knew him said they had never before seen him
so excited. He gave hints, too, that now it would be
easy for him to pay his debts. From a neighbor he
rented a horse and departed for Bordeaux.

What took place in Bordeaux never became known.
Vincent never returned from that journey. In vain
his pupils awaited him, in vain the Duke d'Epernon,
in vain the man from whom he had rented the horse.

There was talk at the time to the effect that a
prominent lady of Toulouse, dying in those days, had
made the young priest her heir, and that this had
occurred while Vincent was on the way to Bordeaux;
and further, that a messenger from Toulouse had set
out to overtake Monsieur Vincent and had caught up
to him halfway between the two cities.

Among the properties of the prominent lady that

awaited Vincent in Toulouse was a note for three or four hundred dollars, the sum she had once loaned to a glib-tongued and careless merchant. He, when he heard of the lady's death and realized that now he would have to repay the loan, fled to Marseilles, the Mediterranean port, to escape being thrown into the debtor's prison. All this the messenger told Vincent, who decided at once not to go on to Bordeaux but to follow the debtor to Marseilles.

Behold now, what was it that had happened to young Monsieur Vincent? Had Satan dangled before the man of grace a benefice, a rich legacy of worldly goods, so that in grasping for it the young priest would plunge into the abyss?

Neither his mother, nor any of the de Paul children, nor anyone else learned what had become of Vincent. He had left for Marseilles, then vanished without leaving a trace.

Chapter III

Pirates, Slavery, and Escape

WHILE his relatives and friends believed that he had come to his death, they knew not how, Monsieur Vincent had gone to Marseilles in pursuit of the debtor. For a moment he had considered returning to Toulouse, but had then told himself that the man owing the money would meanwhile leave Marseilles and be forever beyond his reach. Now three or four hundred dollars was a huge fortune to such as Vincent and he resolved quickly to sell the horse he had rented from a neighbor in Toulouse and use the money to reach Marseilles. Later, upon returning to Toulouse, he would reimburse the neighbor.

In Marseilles Vincent managed to find the man who owed the money. He went to court and caused the glib-tongued and careless merchant to be thrown into a debtor's cell. The man had not reckoned that this would be the outcome of his flight and when he had recovered somewhat from his consternation and saw how serious the situation was, he began to think earnestly on how he could win his release. Brought before the judge, he had to confess that he had borrowed the money, which he carried on his person.

He began at first to make many pleas and false accusations, trying thereby to arouse the pity of the priest. But Monsieur Vincent, who as a boy had given the beggar all of his thirty sous, was suddenly merciless and would not let himself be moved, so that finally the prisoner, seeing no other means of escape, unbuttoned his coat, drew out the moneybag and placed the coins on the table.

The priest Vincent took the money. He counted the coins a few times, smiling the while, then paid the court fees and went away.

Now he stood in a street of Marseilles, a rich man. Suddenly the pressure of care was lifted that had burdened him so many years; aye, his whole life thus far. And with a bag of money in his pocket he found himself changed. He could walk the streets like a man of wealth, buy himself a horse again, ride in a carriage.

It was a hot day and Vincent drank hurriedly of the wine, gazed out at the sea and the sky, then drank again. A new guest came into the inn. To judge by his clothes, he was a nobleman. He looked about, saw that at this hour there was scarcely anyone else in the room, and walked over to the young priest: "With your permission, Monsieur, I will seat myself beside you."

Then he ordered food and drink.

The two fell into a conversation and the nobleman commented on the oppressive heat of the July day. "I would certainly have preferred to return to Bordeaux by land, but because it is so hot it has occurred to me that perhaps it would be wiser to go by boat from here to Narbonne. Out there a cooling breeze is always blowing. It takes a ship one day and one night. How long I would have to ride to cover the distance on land!"

Vincent de Paul said: "I believe God sent you to me. I, too, Monsieur, have finished my business here and am returning to Toulouse. You make a splendid suggestion. If you will permit me to, I will join you and we can go together to find a ship that suits us."

They found each other congenial, for the nobleman could not help but see by the whole bearing of the young priest that he had lived in the homes of the aristocracy and that intercourse with nobles was habitual with him.

So they paid their charges at the inn, went to the docks and found a ship to their liking. The wind was favorable, said the captain; and as the nobleman had surmised, if the wind remained as it was they would reach Narbonne the next day.

"Let us not delay, then," said the titled man, sprang aboard and was followed by Vincent.

As soon as they reached the docks, Vincent encountered an almost unbearable odor. "All ports stink," the nobleman informed him. "It comes from the galley."

And as soon as he trod the ship's deck, in truth the young priest had experienced the smell as an immense wave of something secretively sinister.

This was the first time in his life that he had been on such a vessel. It was a merchant galley, probably eight times as long as wide. At the bow and at the stern the deck was built wider and in the center of the ship Vincent saw a narrow walk running its full length. Along this he followed the nobleman to the upper deck.

But as he hurried on he chanced to glance into the inner part of the ship and saw the galley slaves. Bareheaded men, naked excepting for aprons, their bodies covered with dirt, they sat on their benches and peered at the two passengers on the promenade above them.

Monsieur Vincent heard the rattling of their chains. Four or five were at each oar. There they were chained, exposed to the sun and the tempest, called nothing their own but the small, pear-shaped wooden gags hanging from cords around their necks; but of these Vincent did not know the purpose.

The young priest was frightened by the sight of these men and yet he wished to stop and gaze at them. The nobleman, however, spoke and called to him to follow.

From the other side of the ship came the rumble of a drum and a screamed word, and at once the galley began to move.

Vincent hastened to reach the rear deck and clung to the railing, for the drum had started the rowers' work, turned the ship, and drove it from the haven out into the sea — stroke upon stroke.

He stood at the railing, pale, shaken. His titled companion looked at him and wondered.

"What is the matter, Monsieur?"

"Did you see those men down there?"

Now the nobleman understood.

"Nothing can be done about it. Who else would row the ship?"

From the bridge above the heads of the slaves came an overseer with a whip. He walked back and forth and if he saw an oarsman slacken at his toil, he lashed the man's back with the scourge and bellowed curses at him.

The nobleman began to speak to Vincent, pointed to the shore, identified houses, churches, villages. But the young priest stood as if paralyzed, heard not what was said. The horror he had glimpsed in the slaves' benches lay like a crushing weight upon his spirit.

Meanwhile the port and its shipping had vanished from view. From Marseilles to Narbonne the shore-line makes a northward curve. The galley sought to bear to the west. Soon the hills to the north were lost to sight, too, and Vincent saw that they were surrounded entirely by the sea. He gazed about with eagerness, for now the wonder of the sea was revealed to him for the first time.

"Only a few hours," said the titled man, "and we shall see the Pyrenees again to the west."

"No," answered Vincent, "I see them now, back there."

The other laughed softly. "That is scarcely possible."

"But I see them, three peaks there are. I see them plainly," and he stretched out his arm.

The other tried in vain to see the hills.

Suddenly, then, they heard a curse, the overseer of the slaves cried out, pointed westward, where Vincent said he had seen the three peaks, and immediately the drummer began to beat time for the oarsmen — quicker, quicker the beat of the drum.

From the belly of the ship came the rattling of many chains. The slaves down there had been rowing while seated. Now they stood up, to match the constantly accelerated measure of the drum and give their strokes increased power.

The galley shook and reared.

"By the Devil, what was that?"

Monsieur Vincent still did not know what was happening. Then the nobleman grasped him by the arm. "Damn these rogues!" he shouted and drew his sword.

From out of the west came three galleys with their sails up. Moving swifter than the little merchant ship, they managed to put themselves between the shore and the vessel bound for Narbonne.

They were the galleys of pirates, lurking in these waters to catch vessels along the coast and plunder them.

Three against one.

It did not take long for Monsieur Vincent and his
companion to realize that there was no hope of escape.
The seamen made ready for a battle. But theirs was
a poor ship, with only two small cannons, one each
at prow and stern. The helmsman took command and
tried desperately to break through the three pirate
ships. When the sea robbers had come within shoot-
ing distance, the merchant galley made a quick turn
and at the same instant sent volleys of shot from both
cannons. Then from the corsairs came an outburst
of rage, for one of the volleys had found its mark
straight in the center of one of the three enemy ships.
And the merchant galley turned in flight.

Two of the pirate ships gave chase and were able
to overtake the smaller vessel, force it between the
two of them.

The oars of the merchant vessel were splintered.

In the next instant a hail of shots fell upon the
ship, the first pirates boarded her, knives in their
mouths, curved swords in their fists. It would have
been madness to have attempted resistance.

All this happened so suddenly that Monsieur
Vincent found no time to decide what to do. Ought
he, too, to grasp a weapon?

Before he could do anything he felt a piercing pain
in his hip. An arrow had struck him and more out
of terror than because of the wound, he sank to the
deck. Quickly he gripped the arrow, broke it and
drew the pieces from his flesh, sought with his hands

to stem the flow of blood. Then he looked up.

He saw that the pirates had cut the helmsman to pieces, so furious were they because the merchant ship's cannon had killed one of their leaders, and in this manner they cooled their hot vengeance. They sought, however, to harness their rage and did not kill any other captives after their first anger had passed. For they lurked in these waters not only to gain plunder but also to capture men, whom they took to Tunis to sell into slavery.

Therefore the corsairs soon began to look about, gaze searchingly at their prisoners and bind the wounds of those who had been struck down. They emptied the pockets of their captives of money and other things of value, taking from them even articles of clothing that seemed desirable in their eyes. So Vincent, too, was forced from the deck down into the belly of the ship. There he sat with the galley slaves.

He sat there, still dazed by what had happened, when the first beat of the drum sounded and the rowers gripped their oars and the first stroke began.

Then he heard a curse and over him whirred a lash, hit him in the face.

"Take hold of an oar!" whispered the slave beside him, and at once, like a man beset by tormentors, Vincent stretched out his arms, his hands closed on the oar, he made the motions of the other oarsmen.

For a short time. It seemed to him then that he was losing consciousness. He leaned back.

He heard a curse, again he felt the fierce pain of the whip, he floundered with his hands to grasp the oar but did not find it, as from far away he heard cruel laughter. Then he knew no more.

When Vincent awoke the ship seemed not to be moving. It was dark. The night air lay coolingly upon his cheeks. He felt how a number of welts ran across his face, he tried to reach upward, but that pained him too much, and the dampness bit like salt rubbed into a wound.

The slave at his side sought to raise him up, and whispered, "It will be better soon."

Eventually Vincent heard the beating of the drum once more. It was still night. Someone shoved something to eat into his hands, took away his coat, all his clothes. He sat there naked, like the other slaves.

Once he was bothered by the call of nature. He wished to say something. Then he heard the oarsman beside him laugh.

"He who sits here, my friend, is a galley slave, just as we are. Here we are bound by our chains and around our necks we have the wooden pears. When there's a battle, we must put the gags into our mouths, so we cannot cry out.

"Here we live, here we die — here we sit, here we sleep — here we eat — here we answer the call of nature and our feet stand in our own filth."

For six or seven days the three ships remained at sea, seeking other vessels to capture and plunder, until the pirates were satiated with the newly gained loot.

Then on the morning of the seventh day the vessels stopped and the slaves were brought up from below decks.

Monsieur Vincent saw a strange city, with queer little brown houses huddled closely together. It was like a beehive. From the talk of the men he learned that it was Tunis.

They were taken to the shore, had to wash themselves in the sea. Then each received a cloth that covered only his loins and a brightly colored cap. They were bound together with ropes and driven into the city.

The sea robbers themselves walked ahead and made a tumult, so the people of Tunis would know that new slaves had arrived and that anyone who wished to buy a slave might do so in the market place.

Six or seven times the captives were driven through the streets of the town, then back to the ships.

The buyers had come. The slaves were placed in a row and each was given food, so prospective purchasers might see how they ate. They had been left to suffer hunger, so now they swallowed eagerly what they received.

Finally they were taken to the market place. There they stood in rows and the buyers passed along and one by one the slaves had to step forward to be auctioned.

Those interested in purchasing slaves tested the

captives' arms and legs, grasped them by the chin
and the nose and opened their mouths, as though they
were animals, to see whether their teeth were sound.

Vincent de Paul had to endure all this. He had
to run back and forth to show how agile he was, and
lift heavy objects. They brought another slave to him
and the two had to wrestle. Many times he had to suffer
this ordeal, but all the buyers shook their heads: the
fellow was too weak.

In the end a fisherman bought him and led
him away.

What had become of the nobleman, whether he had
been killed or was among another band of slaves,
Vincent did not know. He had lost sight of him. Now
he had to consider his own fate. The fisherman took
him to the beach, commanded him to enter a little
boat and row out to sea and help him catch fish.

Vincent sat in the boat and did as he was told.
There was no strength of rebellion in him, so much
was he shaken by his misfortunes. Only now and then
he would look up, bewildered, when a blow in the
thigh or a kick in the buttocks sent him to the bottom
of the craft or almost overboard.

He tried, he did all he could to be a good servant
to the fisherman.

Several days passed. Then a cough came from
Vincent's breast and his owner looked at him calculat-
ingly and murmured to himself: "This won't do. It
would be better to sell him in time rather than let

him die here in my boat. He can't endure the sea air."
That evening they came ashore and drew up the boat.
The fisherman took Vincent to a little hut. He knew
a man in the city, to whom he occasionally brought
fish, who needed a slave. One of his workers had died.
This man was a physician of exceptional ability and
well versed in many occult sciences. To him Vincent
was sold by the fisherman.

Vincent, when his master had gone, seated himself
before the hut and looked out over the nocturnal sea.
Then an immense sadness seized him, and for the
first time the terror that had held him seemed to be
loosened and he found words once more. Softly he
began to sing: "*Salve, Regina! Mater misericordiae!*
— Mother of mercy, hail!"

But he could not go on. A deep anguish welled up
in his heart, tears filled his eyes.

Thought seemed to swoon. He managed to cling
to one clear idea: "*Mater misericordiae!*" and recommend himself to Mary's protection.

This was the hour in which the fisherman returned
to the hut and commanded his slave to go with him
to the home of the physician.

Vincent's new master was about 70 years old, and
for more than fifty years he had studied the secrets
of nature. He appeared to be a man of wealth and had
several servants; women, too, were in the house. But
he wished to have a slave who was a stranger in the
land and therefore could not flee, and at the same

time one who could be trusted. For he had a large secret chamber, with twelve ovens that the slave had to watch.

The new master instructed Vincent in all these matters, and soon the slave realized into what a house of mystery he had been sold.

The scientists of those days believed many things concerning nature which we no longer believe. They maintained that there were secret natural forces which the mind of man could not comprehend and which could be evoked only by the use of magic formulas. In those days, physicians employed incantations, but they also knew how to gain healing extracts from plants and animals. However, they believed that this could be done only if the plants were used on specified days, under very special circumstances, and the animals had to be killed in accordance with elaborate mystic regulations. Then they mixed the extracts thus obtained, muttering incantations as they did so, and finally set the mass to boiling.

In this way these physicians of old sought a remedy which they called the elixir of life and of which they believed that if a man drank it, he would be cured of all ailments. In our times men of medicine seek a specific remedy for each disease, but in the days of Vincent's captivity in Tunis they sought a panacea, a single remedy: for they held that evil was the cause of all diseases, that in reality there was but one sickness, that is, evil, which brought death to man. They believed, too, that God had placed the water of life in all plants, all fruit, but intermingled with innumerable poisons, so that their paramount concern was to find a way to extract this life-giving water, obtain it in a pure state.

On these things Vincent's new master had been thinking for fifty years and he had uncovered more than one secret. He had discovered that sickness led to the formation in the human body of stones that caused wounds and eventually proved fatal. He succeeded in concocting a liquid which dissolved the stones until they became like small-grained sand and could be readily eliminated.

After some time, the physician began to tell about and display all these matters to his faithful servant, for he saw that Vincent was devoted to him. He was an alchemist, too, and eager to discover new secrets. He believed that there was a magical white powder, which he called the philosopher's stone, and that if one took quicksilver and spread this powder over it, the mercury would at once be changed into gold. Many other mysterious things were known to him, concerning the mirror of Archimedes and a machine which he called *perpetuum mobile* and which had the power of uninterrupted and unending motion.

Vincent was required to be present when his master gathered the most diverse substances, mixed them and placed them in an oven — and he was present also when, occasionally, the vessels broke with loud crashing and all that was in them was hurled high into the air, and the physician stood aghast at what had happened.

On Vincent's first night in his house the alchemist had asked him what his religion was and he let no day pass without telling the Christian slave of the Mohammedan faith and of the Saracens; for he began to feel a growing affection for Vincent and told him that if he would foreswear his Christian belief, his master was ready to adopt him as his son and reveal to him all the secrets of his science. What could possibly make him happier on earth, he asked his slave?

But Monsieur Vincent served his master faithfully and hoped that Mary, the Mother of Mercy, would rescue him from his captivity and lead him back to his native land.

Since the night in which, in front of the fisherman's hut, he had for the first time after his capture known the solace of the old song, its consolation had never left him. And he cherished in his soul the unshakable faith that he would be liberated.

More than a year passed in this way.

Then there came to the home of the physician and alchemist a messenger with a letter in which the sultan declared that he needed the help of this learned man, who was to prepare at once to come to the court.

Now Vincent's master was an elderly man and although the sultan's command brought high honors with it, he was reluctant to make the journey. However, they started out soon afterwards. In addition to Vincent, who was told to remain at his master's side, all the other slaves accompanied the physician, leaving only as many as were necessary to guard his home. The route, on a pitilessly hot day, lay along a chain of hills at the edge of the desert.

Then, on the third day, the physician succumbed to the rigors of the journey. Weeping, for he had learned to love this master, Vincent brought the body back to Tunis.

What would happen now?

The very next day a young heir came and took possession of the house and of the slaves, and when Vincent was brought before him he was asked from what land he came. He said he came from France, and thereat the face of the heir betrayed momentary concern and he looked thoughtfully at the slave. This did not escape the eye of Monsieur Vincent, who was later to learn the meaning of it.

At that time arrangements were being made to send to Tunis an envoy to demand in the name of the King of France the liberation of all Christian slaves taken from French ships by the pirates. The heir possibly knew of this and that it might lead to the loss of this slave, so he gave thought to evading the loss. He was acquainted with a rich man living on a vast estate farther inland, and to him he sent a messenger and sold Vincent. The new master of Vincent de Paul was Guillaume Gautier. He had been a Franciscan friar

who like Vincent was captured and sold to a rich
Mohammedan. But he renounced the faith of his
fathers and became a renegade, as they called the
Christians who adopted the creed of Islam.

Gautier the renegade had succeeded in winning the
affection of his master, who adopted him as his son
and heir. Now the erstwhile friar lived beyond Tunis
on his estate in the hills, lived like a true Musselman
and sought to wipe out all memories of what he had
been. He had a number of wives, among them a Greek
who had been a nun, and there was an especially close
bond between these two: both Gautier and his favorite
wife suffered the torment of a faith denied.

Among the other wives was a Turkish woman who
seemed to have fathomed her husband's secret. She
noticed that when Vincent came into the house, Gautier had him summoned a number of times, but always
afterwards caused this slave to be sent to a distant field
of the estate, where he was forced to pull a plow like
an ox. It seemed to the Turkish woman that Gautier
banished Vincent as far as possible because for some
reason the presence of this Christian slave troubled
him.

Now this woman began to feel a strange affection for
Vincent and for many days she sought an opportunity
to go out into the fields, as if by accident, in order to
observe him and perhaps learn from him the final
secret of her husband's life. She had often asked the
renegade about the faith he had once professed, which

he had abandoned; for there lived in her a secret, unquenchable yearning for the religion of Christ.

One day Vincent was alone in a field, lying exhausted against the plow he had drawn through many furrows. The Turkish woman came to him and commanded the servant who accompanied her to bring Vincent a refreshing drink; and then she bade the slave sing a song.

"I have heard, often, how you have sung in secret and I love your voice. I should like to hear the song you sing so often, and you shall tell me what it means."

Vincent gazed at her sadly and shook his head.

Again the woman bade him sing.

An indescribable grief flooded the heart of Vincent then and he began to sing in a monotone of infinite sadness:

"*Quomodo cantabimus in terra aliena?*" —

"How shall we sing the song of the Lord in a strange land?" And he chanted the 136th Psalm:

> "*Super flumina Babylonis,*
> *illic sedimus et flevimus,*
> *cum recordaremur Sion.*
> Upon the rivers of Babylon,
> there we sat and wept:
> when we remembered Sion."

When he ceased singing, the Turkish woman said: "Oh, that I could send you back to your home! But there is another song I have heard you sing, one that does not complain but is a solace in utter loneliness. Why do you complain when you have that solace?"

That caused Vincent to smile, and with tears still in his eyes he began to sing:

"*Salve, Regina, mater misericordiae*" — and thus to the end.

"Who is this Queen?"

Then he began to tell her of the Christian faith.

That evening the Turkish woman went to her husband and spoke thus to him: "Why do you keep from me the secrets of your belief? Now I have discovered them and I cannot understand why you surrendered the precious treasure of life, which every slave may possess and through which he is much richer than you. I cannot understand why you surrendered your faith for these fields and this outward wealth, these rugs and jewels, which are no more than a beautiful garment, while the worm of conscience gnaws in your soul. Why do you not restore health to your spirit and purchase eternal life by surrendering your estate? Were I a Christian, I would never have done what you did."

Thereupon the renegade Guillaume Gautier was overwhelmed by an immense spiritual anguish and all that he had suppressed through the years now burst forth from his heart. He caused Vincent to be brought to him, embraced the slave as soon as he crossed the threshold, called him his brother and told him that, while remaining outwardly a slave in the fields, he was to prepare in secret to flee with his master. They were surrounded by spies and the utmost caution was necessary.

Vincent marveled at all this, but he realized now how he would be rescued. It was through his Mother's song.

Soon the master drew Vincent from the fields back into the house, so they might the better take counsel concerning their flight. But it was ten months before they could finally make their escape in a small boat, the renegade and his two wives and the slave Vincent.

On the 28th of June in the year 1607 the surf brought their craft ashore on the French coast at a place called Aiguesmortes. Thence they made a pilgrimage to Avignon, on the Feast of the Apostles Peter and Paul.

There were many strangers in Avignon and the news of these unusual refugees from Tunis spread with lightninglike speed among the people, and the vice-legate of the Pope sent a messenger to their lodgings and had them brought into his presence. He bade them tell him the story of their escape.

The renegade Gautier confessed to the vice-legate and was received back into the bosom of the Church and the two women were received into the Church, too, and afterwards entered a convent.

More than the others did the papal legate question Vincent de Paul concerning his experiences as a slave in Tunis. He was particularly inquisitive about the secrets of nature Monsieur Vincent had learned from

the Mohammedan physician and alchemist; most of all
the remedies he had concocted. He was keenly interested, too, in the fabled mirror of Archimedes and
wished to know the secret of the "speaking skull" in
the witches' kitchen where Vincent had tended the
twelve ovens.

When Vice-Legate Montorio left Avignon for Rome
shortly after this, he induced the young priest Vincent
de Paul and Guillaume Gautier to accompany him.

In Rome the converted renegade joined the Brothers
of Mercy to do penance for his sins.

But Monsieur Vincent was kept close to the vice-
legate who bade him be always in readiness for a
mission, the purpose and nature of which he would
reveal to him at the proper time.

Chapter IV

THE SECRET WORD

FROM Avignon Vincent had written a letter to his mother to let her know that he still lived. And as soon as the wave of curiosity that surrounded him in Avignon subsided, he wrote also to his generous patron, Monsieur de Comet, on the 24th of July, 1607, telling him the adventure of his slavery in Tunis. Later, from Rome, he wrote a second letter to Monsieur de Comet, on the 28th of February, 1608, also concerning his captivity; and both of these letters have been preserved.

Meanwhile Vincent lived in Rome at the house of his new friend, Vice-Legate Montorio. He withdrew as much as possible, visited the sacred places, knelt and prayed at the tombs of the Princes of the Apostles and descended to the graves in the catacombs, where he was infused with the glowing faith of the many who had for Christ's sake suffered martyr deaths. This filled him with solace and with sadness both. Down there they slept peacefully in their graves. Above ground the generations of living men — who among them now led with the banner of Christ's kingdom, what armies followed the cross, athirst and ahunger for naught but the deeds of our Saviour's eight Beatitudes?

From the world there penetrated even into the catacombs such a tumult as seemed almost to be like the
rage of Hell, so that Vincent desired intensely to remain down there and when evening came returned
with reluctance to the residence of the vice-legate, who
like a secular official often held feasts of worldly pomp,
at which the simple son of Gascony peasants — Monsieur Vincent, thus they called him — was led by his
host into the midst of the cardinals and other eminent
guests and asked to tell of his captivity in Africa and
most of all of the old alchemist whose twelve ovens
Vincent had fired for his master's magic arts.

Once, when Vincent had succeeded in withdrawing
from the curiosity of the guests at such a feast, and
from a niche in the sumptuous hall was gazing wearily
at the crowd, an eminent personage approached him
from behind and placed a hand on his shoulder.

Vincent was startled.

"May I have a word with you?" asked the stranger.
"You are a Frenchman?"

Then Monsieur Vincent noticed that the man spoke
the language of his native land.

"Trust me. I am the Marquis de Breves, the envoy
of the King of France. I have seen you here a number
of times, without your being aware of it. Are you not
homesick? I seemed to detect in you a sense of not
feeling at home here. Would you not like to go to
Paris?"

Vincent de Paul looked at the Marquis and did not

know what answer to make, for he understood full well that there was much more to the ambassador's words than appeared on the surface.

"You impress me as a man worthy of the utmost confidence," continued the Marquis, "therefore I shall come to the point at once and tell you what the business is.

"I have a message for my master, the King of France, which I cannot trust to any document. I seek a messenger who can travel inconspicuously from Rome to Paris with a password which I will give him, and in this way gain audience with the king in his palace and deliver to His Majesty the word which no other person in the world may hear.

"If you will perform this service for your native land, I shall expect you tomorrow morning at the third hour in my residence. You will have no difficulty finding where I live.

"Now I shall leave you without a formal farewell. We might be noticed and no one must be given even the slightest intimation that I have chosen you for this mission. I trust you."

The Marquis de Breves acted as though he had conferred a little courtesy upon his compatriot whose experiences were the subject of so much gossip, then he mixed again in the throng of guests.

Chapter V

THE JUDGE'S MONEYBAG

MONSIEUR VINCENT DE PAUL appeared in
Paris toward the close of the year 1608; appeared as a
stranger, a humble traveler from the provinces who
had come to behold for once the life of the court, as
many came to gain the patronage of powerful person-
ages and thus achieve a dignity or an office.

Vincent had parted from his friend and patron, the
Vice-Legate Montorio, some months previously in
Rome, saying he wished to return to his native land,
where the Church was in dire need. There he wished
to be a simple laborer in the Lord's vineyard.

Paris, which the knowing ones of the times called a
den of beasts, was the great royal fortress of France.
Huddled within its walls lay the inner city. On both
banks of the Seine, where the river entered the city
and where it left it, mighty square towers had been
built and from tower to tower over the mirroring
water hung gigantic chains, so that only the ships
which the watchman permitted to do so could pass up
or down the stream.

Everything in this city was arranged to wage fierce
wars of defense and repulsion.

Like a solitary shrine, a legacy of ancient days, stood the Church of Notre Dame; like a fairy castle hedged about, it stood in the city which had forgotten the spirit of the fathers who had built this sanctuary of faith.

When Monsieur Vincent reached Paris he sought quarters, but avoiding the city whose frowning bulwarks made an unpleasant impression upon him, he chose the suburb of Saint-Germain-des-Prés, westward of Paris. It was an old village of bad roads full of morasses. The houses were low and black, crouched in gardens and orchards, vineyards and meadows.

A canal called the Little Seine curved about the village. In a street named the Seine and near the Brothers of Mercy Hospital called the Charité, Monsieur Vincent found modest lodgings. Without being fully aware of the reason, he felt a desire to be close to the Charité, so he knocked at the door of one of the first houses in the street, to ask whether a room were for rent there.

A peasant opened the door, looked with some astonishment at the stranger, and said "No, no!"

But a woman came out of the kitchen, a stout but active housewife, wiping her hands on her apron and asking what the matter was. Without waiting for an answer, for she had guessed, she managed the withdrawal of her husband as one who did not understand, and then invited the young priest to enter.

To be sure they had a room, an attractive one, which

they would gladly put at their guest's disposal at a small rental, and she urged Monsieur Vincent into the room. It was poor and small, but the window looked out upon the Seine and it suited Vincent well.

Then the man followed his wife and declared that the room could not be rented to the stranger because it was already rented to Monsieur the Judge.

The woman told him to be silent, said he understood nothing, resumed her air of friendliness toward the young priest. He wished to leave, but she urged him to wait, repeating that her husband knew nothing.

Yes, it was true, the judge from Sore had rented the room, but he came only occasionally from the village near Bordeaux to transact his business in Paris. He was not here now and when he came again she would see to it that the two gentlemen got along all right in the room. How easy it would be to set up another bed! And Monsieur the Priest would find it better to live here, for he would pay twice as much elsewhere. The judge shared the rental of this room.

And thus she persuaded Monsieur Vincent to take the lodgings.

In the presence of her husband she put her hand to her forehead, to indicate her estimate of his mental powers. Would the judge in Bordeaux know who had his room here in Saint-Germain?

Monsieur Vincent did not know how long he would stay. Perhaps he would have to leave Paris again very shortly.

That very evening the priest returned to the city and went to the palace of the King, and when the sentinels stopped him he spoke a secret word, the word the Marquis de Breves had confided to him. At this the guards gazed at him in astonishment and he was conducted into the interior of the royal palace.

He remained at the palace several hours. Night had fallen when he left. Tired, he returned to his room in Saint-Germain-des-Prés and there he remained.

The woman of the house sought to spy on Monsieur Vincent. But the quiet man, who was a priest, prayed his Breviary, and except for this there was nothing unusual about him. She told him many things he might see in the city and even out here in Saint-Germain. He, however, seemed to be content to sit in silence, pray his Office and take long walks in the gardens and meadows.

This impressed the housewife. Priests were not, as a class, held in high esteem. The whole land had been devastated by the decades of civil wars fought for religion's sake. Throughout France churches lay in ruins, the altars shattered, the images smashed. Where were priests to be seen, even at long intervals? More than one devout priest had fled to the solitude of a village in the hills, where an ancient shrine had escaped destruction.

There would have been no priests at all in those days if no benefices had survived from the past. The churches and monasteries retained the ancient rights to feudal service or income, and not of divine service, and the incomes were still sought after. Many a one became an abbot at that time to support his kin among the nobles on the monastery's revenues, and it was held to be almost an insult to make a priest an abbot.

The State had incurred stupendous debts because of the many wars, so the King himself and the nobles were eager to gorge themselves on the surviving goods of the Church. It was said that close to the King was many a marquis wearing around his neck a costly chain made from the gold of stolen chalices and monstrances and set with precious stones which the wearer had torn from ancient reliquaries.

Where was there still a priest who prayed? All of them seemed submerged in the trade of the world.

However, at the Charité a few quixotic men survived. They called themselves Brothers of Mercy and instead of striving for benefices they trudged the muddy streets of Paris, seeking out the sick and the helpless and bringing them to their house in Saint-Germain and there enveloping them and caring for them with Christian love.

Queer, this newly come priest who prayed and seemed to be waiting, said the housewife to herself.

She told him one day that if he wished to take a walk, westward along the Seine, in the same street in which he lodged and only a few hundred steps away, was the new palace of Queen Marguerite of Valois.

"Marguerite of Valois?"

Monsieur Vincent felt a strange tremor pass through him at the mention of that name, and his eyes were like those of a wondering child.

Yes, yes, did he not know, began the woman? The Queen had returned to Paris about three years ago. She had been gone twenty-five years and now three years since a new palace had been built for her here in the Rue de Seine. Four years ago there had been a woods on the site, and as if by magic in a short time the woods had been transformed into the royal park. Many came from Paris and even from distances to stand in front of the park and catch glimpses of the fabulous lives of the great ones of the world. Oh, Queen Marguerite is a beautiful, stately woman!

"How long ago that was!" said Monsieur Vincent to himself, forgetting that the housewife was present. A terrifying memory of his boyhood seized him. Marguerite of Valois, she was the Queen of whom his father had sung the sinister song of St. Bartholomew's Day and the bloody wedding.

"She must have been beautiful beyond all telling," the woman continued. "Now, she is about 56 years old. The bloody wedding of St. Bartholomew's night, that, Monsieur, was 37 years ago."

"They have been unjust to her," the housewife went on. "Our King, Henry IV, believed Queen Marguerite to blame for the massacre. But that is not true. Her mother, Monsieur, she was a bad woman. She had the devil in her body. She caused the murdering. And

Queen Marguerite has no children, so the King had to give her up on that account, because of an heir to the throne. That was ten years ago.

"They say, I know, that our Queen Marguerite had more than one little devil in her heart, when she was young. They say she lived frivolously, and that troubled the King. Did he have any right to be vexed? Doesn't he live, too, and frivolously? The devil knows how."

The woman was full of gossip. Monsieur Vincent arose. "Let us not speak evil of them. Let us seek, rather, the good in others, Madame."

But the gossip continued to pour forth in a swollen stream.

Queen Marguerite keeps a court here in Saint-Germain. She delights in having learned men and poets and painters and sculptors about her, and in providing great feasts. "I assure you, Monsieur, she is wonderfully beautiful, even now, Monsieur. And if she sins, doesn't she do penance, too? Doesn't she go to Mass every day and to Communion three times a month? Isn't she generous to the poor? And even when she makes a royal offering, she always says 'Oh, forgive me because it is such a little thing.' She begs the beggar for pardon, no matter how munificent her gift.

"For this reason, Monsieur, we love the Queen here in Saint-Germain, and if the King wished to do her justice, because he deposed her, we could tell him many things about the one he has now."

"Please stop! It is not right to seek out the evil in our neighbors," said Vincent; and walked out into the street.

"Only a few hundred steps!" the woman cried out after him, "down the left there and you will be at the entrance to the gardens."

For a moment Monsieur Vincent stood in indecision, then turned to the right and went to the hospital of the Brothers of Mercy.

A few days later a messenger came from the royal court. Unfortunately, Monsieur was not at home but at the Charité, doing what he loved so much to do, helping to care for the poor and sick.

The woman from whom Vincent rented his room was almost beside herself with excitement and curiosity. Oh, this strange guest in her house! She had from the first suspected that there was a mystery about him! He was so modest, so free from any demands on life, there must be something exceptional about him. And now this messenger from the court of the King!

She ran in advance of the messenger to the Charité and called from a distance for Monsieur Vincent and looked amazed when Vincent heard the news with complete calmness and quietly followed the court courier.

That evening the judge from Sore came to the house in the Rue de Seine, unexpectedly. The housewife knew how to tell him that she regretted having put another guest in the room with him, but it could not be avoided. A young priest, but only apparently that. He was in the confidence of the King and a servant from the court had requested the lodgings for him, had insisted that the priest named Vincent de Paul live in the Seine street. How could she, the poor peasant, know why the King wished to have Monsieur Vincent lodge in this street, in her house? What could she do? Could she have refused to admit this priest for whom a royal servant sought a room? Perhaps he was sent to investigate something concerning the life of the deposed Queen? One could not even guess what mission he had. He goes about mysteriously and every few days is summoned secretly to the palace of the King.

But Monsieur the Judge was not to take any notice of all this, for Monsieur Vincent would admit nothing, would discuss nothing. He tried frankly to keep everything secret, let nobody know what he did, as though he were merely a simple person, a harmless priest.

And so the landlady believed that she would do the judge a favor if she gave him such an influential man as roommate.

The judge, who was as inquisitive as he was loquacious, as some lawyers are inclined to be, was at first put out at discovering that he had to share the room with another; but soon he began to praise the woman and assure her that he would get along very well with the other lodger.

Some hours later Vincent returned to the room and

when the two men found that both were Gascons, they experienced this as a mutual pleasure in their absence from the native province.

The judge sent the landlady at once to fetch wine. Monsieur Vincent protested laughingly, gesturing with both hands, but the new friendship had to be properly pledged, said the man of the law. Soon Vincent needed not to talk at all as he sat opposite the judge. He felt cheerful, as one who has had a fortunate day, for whom all things proceed satisfactorily. The judge tried to tell Monsieur Vincent all sorts of things, sought to press his friendship upon the priest; and as Monsieur did not drink the judge from Sore drank twice as much, until late into the night. Then the two men prepared to go to sleep. The woman had set up a second bed.

Monsieur Vincent had announced that he would seek another lodging, that he felt like an intruder. The judge, however, begged him to remain. Was he not a poor priest and in addition to that, a Gascon? He was glad to have him as a roommate; and in his heart he thought, perhaps you can some day do me a service at the court, and that will repay me a hundredfold.

A few times more Monsieur Vincent was summoned by the King, then no more.

Nor was he told more than this, that in the matter concerning which he had spoken to none other, he was to hold himself in readiness. It was possible that His Majesty would wish to employ him further in the matter.

So Monsieur Vincent waited and when he was not praying he walked, one day, along the Seine street toward the palace of Queen Marguerite, for within him was a secret longing to see with his living eyes the woman with whom he had fallen in love in his boyish years, because she had appeared to him in the tragic glory of the bloody wedding of St. Bartholomew's Day.

It came to pass that now and then he would meet a few priests who came from the Queen's palace and were returning to Paris. And when he had met them a second time, and a third, they must have wondered: Who is he? For some time he has been seen in this street. Does he live here, what does he wish? But they passed by.

Once, too, when Monsieur Vincent was helping to nurse the sick at the Charité, one of these priests came there. "Who is he?," Vincent asked a Brother of Mercy, quietly.

The other priest was apparently some six years older than Vincent, and undoubtedly of noble lineage, for in all he did, his walk, the movements of his hands, his speech, he gave evidence of high birth.

"He is the priest Pierre de Bérulle. Do you not know him?" asked the Brother. "Let me tell you, though the Church of France lies shattered, among those who will raise her up he is one of the mightiest.

"Is there a Huguenot whom you wish to convince that his creed is false, send him to Cardinal Duperron, who will convince him, so that thereafter he will believe otherwise, in his mind. And is there a Huguenot whom you wish to convert, so that he will actually live a holy life, send him to the Bishop Francois de Sales. But if there is a Huguenot whom you wish to convince and also convert, send him to Monsieur de Bérulle. There is no greater one, none more eloquent in all France."

Monsieur Pierre de Bérulle, having noticed the simple peasant priest, approached Vincent, asked him his name, where he lived, and conversed with him regarding the sick, then left the hospital.

At another time another priest came to the Charité with Monsieur de Bérulle. He carried a large bag and divided its contents among the sick.

Monsieur Vincent saw this remarkable visitor from some distance, and one of the Brothers of Mercy whispered to him: "That is Monsieur Charles du Fresne. He is the private secretary of Queen Marguerite of Valois and it is at her command that he distributes these alms."

The two priests approached, stood before Vincent de Paul. Monsieur de Bérulle addressed Vincent and introduced him to the Queen's secretary, saying, while he laughed gently, that the sick had no more devoted nurse than Monsieur Vincent, though he actually did not belong to the Charité. "I have seen him care for the sick a number of times. I believe there is no man with gentler hands, none whose glance can see a need more quickly, Monsieur du Fresne." Then the two went their way. They met each other more than once thereafter.

Once Monsieur de Bérulle remarked to Monsieur Vincent: Near here (at a place which he described) a number of priests meet from time to time, at a specified hour on certain days, to discuss the dire needs of their native land and of their Church and to lighten their hearts by mutual consolation. If Monsieur would join this circle, Monsieur de Bérulle would be pleased indeed.

Happy, Vincent de Paul thanked him; and henceforth, as often as the priests gathered, the modest young one from Pouy was in their midst.

Autumn had come and with it from the marshes of the Seine an epidemic fever, so that the Charité was soon overflowing with the sick. Monsieur Vincent had his hands full. Then the fever struck him, too, and one morning he was so weak that he fell back upon the bed when he tried to get up.

The judge from Sore, still lodging with him, said: "Well, my honored friend, there is nothing to do but to stay in bed. On my way to the city I will stop at the apothecary's and tell him to send you a fever cure."

Vincent nodded. He was so weak that he gladly accepted any help.

Then the judge left the room.

A few hours passed, which Vincent spent sitting up in bed. His hands, which he had folded in prayer, were clasped tightly together and he wrung them in agony, so intense was the feverish burning in his body. The prayers he prayed and the thoughts he thought began to lose all meaning.

Occasionally the landlady came and sat by his bedside, but she was sadly disillusioned. For some time, no messenger from the royal court had come to her house. The judge had tried repeatedly to uncover the secret of Monsieur Vincent and had even more than once reproached the woman with having invented the story of the King's courier. No one could help but see that Vincent was a poor fellow, with scarcely enough for such a living as his was. He who is summoned to the court and received by the King, surely he is given at least enough money to buy more than a piece of dry bread. When does Monsieur Vincent drink wine? It cannot be true, what the woman told him about this roommate of his. The judge from Sore began to have his suspicions.

Nor did it escape Vincent's notice that the friendliness of the man of law and the eagerness of the landlady had ebbed. He thought on this, now that he lay sick. When he regained his health he would leave the house.

Through the veil which the fever wound about him, he looked up. Was someone in the room?

The apothecary's boy had brought the medicine.

Monsieur Vincent's hand trembled as he put it forth to take the remedy.

"Is there a glass here?" asked the boy.

Monsieur Vincent told the apprentice to ask the landlady. Or perhaps there was a glass in the cupboard. The judge kept his wine bottles there, perhaps there would be a glass by them.

The lad went to the cabinet, opened it. He stared at what he saw.

"Is there no glass?" asked the sick man, hesitant and impatient at the same time.

The voice from the bed startled the apprentice.

"A moment, I shall see!"

He had seen the glass at once, but also, beside it, a moneybag, and that he had grabbed.

"I shall see! I shall see!" and he rummaged through the cupboard, the while slipping the bag into his pocket.

"Ah, here's a glass!" he said at last, as though only then discovering the vessel. He hurried to the bed and poured out the medicine.

Why was the lad in such a tremendous hurry? Why was he pouring too much medicine into the glass?

But the fever racked Monsieur Vincent so violently that he was not able to distinguish things clearly. He put out a trembling hand for the glass and drank its contents, handed the vessel back to the boy, scarcely feeling how it slipped from his fingers, then sank back upon the pillow.

How long did he lie there? Suddenly he felt himself shaken, heard his name called.

He aroused himself abruptly. "What is it?" Confusedly he sought to orientate himself. "What do you wish?"

At the foot of the bed stood his roommate, the judge, all wrought up.

It was the morning after the one on which Vincent had failed to leave his bed. The judge, returning to the room late at night, had found the priest asleep. It is well for him to sleep, sleep himself back to health!

Monsieur Vincent was still asleep the next morning. The judge dressed himself, prepared to go to the city again. Today he would transact some business and needed to have money with him. He went to the cupboard, opened the door.

"Where is the moneybag? It is not here!"

An abject fear gripped him. He shook the sick man awake.

"Where is the bag, the moneybag?"

Vincent did not understand.

"Tell me, where is my money? Has someone been here?"

Still the sick man did not understand. "No," he said.

"What is that? No one has been here? You have been alone in the room? You only? My moneybag is gone — my 400 dollars! Do not jest about it! Did you hide the money?"

"I do not understand," said the sick priest.

"You do not understand what I am saying?"

This infuriated the judge.

"You shall understand! By the devil, look at this fellow! He feigns sickness, so he can be alone in the room, I forget to lock the cupboard, a single time I forget to lock it, and the money is gone! But let me tell you, you shall reveal where you have hidden it, you rascal!"

And the judge from Sore began to shout, called the landlady, screamed at her:

"Now see whom you put in this room with me! A confidant of the King, eh? A fine confidant of His Majesty! A thief, my good woman, a money snatcher! While I was in Paris he plundered my cupboard."

"Mon Dieu!" screamed the woman, and made a gesture of incredulity.

But the judge continued to rage and would not stop until Vincent, the feverish man, arose and dressed himself.

He would throw him out, this rogue; he would go to the court of justice, he would have him put into prison, he would not rest until he had his 400 dollars back; he, the judge from Sore.

Like a fugitive, Monsieur Vincent staggered weakly along the street to the Charité, where for the present he would stay with the Brothers.

Soon the judge followed and his shouts sounded in the hospital corridors.

"Where is he, the rascal? Where is the money grabber?"

And in the presence of the Brothers and of the sick he accused the young priest anew of theft and demanded that Monsieur Vincent admit his guilt.

Vincent, however, knew nothing to say but this: "God knows, I do not." Thereupon the Brothers bade the embittered, shouting judge leave their house.

Monsieur Vincent, too, arose and would have left the place. The terror he endured because of the judge's fierce denunciation had driven the fever from his body. But the Brothers took hold of him, induced him to remain.

Vincent gazed around at the sick. Not one of them believed the judge. He saw it in their eyes. They believed him innocent, therefore he would stay.

Had not Monsieur du Fresne, private secretary to Queen Marguerite of Valois, stopped in the street to talk with this rascally Monsieur Vincent? Now Monsieur du Fresne was coming up the street, and the judge in his room saw him approaching. At once he sprang to the street and detained the secretary and asked him whether he had heard this about Monsieur Vincent, the thief.

Monsieur du Fresne was amazed: "But, Monsieur, how can you believe that?"

"I shall prove it to you!" shouted the raging man. "I shall prove that what I say is true!"

Those who had come to love Monsieur Vincent asked him, "Was anyone else in the room? Tell us! Defend yourself!"

"How shall I defend myself if God does not defend me?"

"Who else could it have been, then?"

Vincent knew only that a boy had come into the room. A boy — he surely could not involve him. How could such a one defend himself?

And in answer to all urging, he said: "God only knows."

The judge from Sore ran to the Bishop of Paris.

One afternoon when Monsieur de Bérulle and his priestly friends were gathered at his house for one of the conferences of the brotherhood they had formed, and Monsieur Vincent was there, a tumult arose, the door was flung open and the judge burst into the room.

In the presence of Monsieur de Bérulle and the entire Sacred College assembled there he accused Vincent de Paul of theft, using many ugly words; and then he displayed a letter from the Bishop of Paris in which the judge is commanded to do all that is possible to bring the thief to justice. The letter was to be posted on the doors of all the churches!

"My dear friend," said Monsieur de Bérulle to Monsieur Vincent, who stood silently in their midst, "now you must defend yourself! Who could have been in the room; who besides yourself? Why do you not say that you were dazed by drinking the medicine? Did perhaps the apothecary's apprentice who brought you the medicine . . . ? Did he have anything to do at the cupboard? The glass, did he perhaps . . . ?"

Vincent made a gesture of refusal. "Who could accuse a child?"

And raging, the judge from Sore left the room.

Six years later Monsieur the Judge was called to a prison in Bordeaux. A prisoner who had become ill and feared that he would die, wished urgently to speak with him.

Going to the prison, he found a youth who approached him on his knees and implored him to listen and to forgive.

"Six years ago, Monsieur, do you remember, in Paris, you accused a priest, Monsieur Vincent de Paul . . ."

"Don't mention that rogue's name!" shouted the judge.

"He is a saint, Monsieur! You have done him a grave injustice, for it was I who stole your 400 dollars."

The young prisoner told the amazed judge the whole story. He was the apothecary's apprentice who had seen the bag and stolen it when he went to the cupboard to get a glass.

After the theft, the apprentice had fled to Bordeaux and there he had stolen again, but this time the law had caught him, and now, having become sick in the pestilential prison and nearing death, he wished to make what amends he could.

The judge from Sore staggered out of the prison like a drunken man. He wrote a letter to Monsieur

Vincent, begging the priest to forgive him. If he refused, the judge would come to Paris with a halter around his neck and trudge through the streets of the city and accuse himself, aloud, until Monsieur Vincent forgave him.

When Vincent read this letter he smiled a happy smile. Then he sat himself down and wrote to the judge, saying he had forgiven him years ago and there was no need of a pilgrimage of penance. He added that Another, infinitely more innocent, had taken upon Himself and carried an infinitely heavier burden of guilt.

Chapter VI

QUEEN MARGUERITE'S ALMONER

SOON after the accusation of theft against Monsieur Vincent had begun to spread among the people of Saint-Germian-des-Prés, Monsieur du Fresne, the private secretary of Marguerite of Valois came to him, to tell him that he, like Monsieur de Bérulle, was convinced of his innocence. He came to the young priest in the new lodgings he had found, as modest as the first ones, and told him that Queen Marguerite had been informed of the matter of the judge's money but also of Monsieur Vincent's love-inspired devotion to the sick and poor at the Charité. And for this reason the Queen sent her private secretary to him, asking him to visit her.

Monsieur Vincent pressed one hand hard into the other and was silent. He only nodded and, as he was, started out with Monsieur du Fresne into the street that led to the royal park.

Jubilant sounds came from the palace grounds. The Queen was not celebrating a feast, but all days were festive when she was in her gardens surrounded by the learned men, the poets, the artists who sought her patronage.

When Monsieur du Fresne arrived accompanied by the simple priest, many in the circle looked with mistrust at the peasant, for they were always at pains to simulate the nobility which they did not possess.

The Queen, seated in the midst of a group of savants disputing for her entertainment, looked up a garden path and saw Monsieur du Fresne approaching. She gave the learned men a signal to cease speaking and to withdraw somewhat, for she was about to receive a new guest. No, she changed her mind, let them stay. The courtiers drew back a little, remaining near enough to see and hear.

The private secretary led the young priest to the Queen, who looked at him with graciousness and a keen curiosity. There was as it were a hunger about her mouth.

Vincent bowed before her and bent his knee, as the custom was, and rose to his feet when her hand motioned him to do so. He stood, waiting for her to speak.

"You are Monsieur Vincent?"

He looked at her. Now he saw that she was fair, still more beautiful than any other, and she was a queen. Thus he had thought of her.

But his eyes were calm and confident, like those of a child, a boy, and he felt no shyness.

She was aware of this and wondered at it.

"They have told me about you."

He began to let his eyes read her face. At first

he had felt a great happiness at seeing this woman. Now he saw that a fear lurked in her eyes. And she was aware of the scrutiny of his eyes.

"Whence do you come, Monsieur Vincent?"

"From Pouy. There my father was a peasant farmer, my mother a peasant woman, my Royal Lady. And my first work was to herd swine."

The favorites close by looked at each other and their lips began to curve in sneering smiles. But they looked at Queen Marguerite, to see whether they dared betray their mockery.

Marguerite of Valois was sunk in thought.

Then she said: "Now I know, Monsieur Vincent. You tended the animals and loved even them in their helplessness. How much more do you know how to love human beings who are in need, and how to guard them like poor lost animals. I have a favor to ask of you."

She spoke hesitantly, as though she were still weighing the matter. Before this quiet man who asked nothing at all of her, in the midst of the courtiers who had come only to display their learning or their art before her in rivalry for her favors, the Queen had become uncertain, and she felt the presence of a purity which stirred her soul to its depths.

"Who, Monsieur Vincent," continued the queen, "who does not need to do penance?"

Vincent knew this woman was accused of having led a frivolous life from her youth to the present, and in her heart she clung to some sins. Now she felt age coming on.

He knew she went to Mass daily, received the Bread of Angels each month, and still she fell again into sin — and still she came, again and again, to the altar of cleansing.

"I wish to ask you, Monsieur Vincent, to be my almoner and as such enter my service. I am troubled lest the little I am able to give to the poor and the sick may not always reach the proper hands. I need someone to help me, one who knows how to separate the needy from the unworthy. Will you come?"

Monsieur Vincent sank on one knee and bowed his head to show his compliance with her request.

"All other matters Monsieur du Fresne will tell you." The Queen nodded and so dismissed him.

The talk of the learned men and artists and poets, silenced for a space, began anew now that the Queen rejoined their circle.

From that day Monsieur Vincent as Queen Marguerite's almoner walked the narrow alleys and visited the hovels of Paris and went out into the suburban villages, doing good wherever he could.

Second Book: Among the Lowly and the Great

The young galley slave is freed by Vincent.

Chapter VII

THE DARK NIGHT OF THE SOUL

AT THE beginning of the year 1610 King Henry IV
of France gave Monsieur Vincent the Cistercian abbey
of Saint Léonard de Chaumes, to which large revenues
were attached. It was gossiped about that Queen
Marguerite had had a hand in obtaining this honor
and assured income for her almoner.

Monsieur Vincent scarcely took notice of the abbacy.
He remained in Paris, remained the Queen's almoner,
and what of worldly riches came to him, he put in the
same treasury in which lay the Queen's alms, which
he continued to distribute among the poor and
the sick.

However, a few weeks after Monsieur Vincent had
been given the abbacy, a great feast was celebrated
in Paris. King Henry had taken a second wife, Marie
de Medici, ten years after the repudiation of Queen
Marguerite and the Pope's decision that the King's
marriage to her had been entered into under com-
pulsion and was therefore null and void. But the
second marriage, too, failed to be a happy one. The
desires of the King and those of his second queen ran
contrariwise, and each went a separate way. But Marie

de Medici had given King Henry an heir, a baby boy
who would one day as King Louis XIII succeed his
father on the throne of France.

The times were filled with rumors of threatening
wars and the learned men and artists and poets at the
court of Marguerite of Valois had much to talk about.
King Henry had in mind to break the power of the
House of Hapsburg and weld the nations of Europe
into one Christian union of States under France's
leadership. He would conquer the princes who
resisted, shed the glory of his throne upon the willing
ones, and Europe would be one great empire.

But before the King went forth to wage these wars,
the solemn crowning of Queen Marie was to be
celebrated in Paris. She had been the King's wife for
ten years, had given him and the country an heir to
the throne, but had neither borne the diadem nor
been solemnly crowned. The King had until now
opposed the bestowal of this final, highest honor upon
the Queen, his wife though she was, and he saw the
coronation day draw near with forebodings. A sinister
intimation was in him that this "damned celebration,"
as he expressed it, would cause his death. And so it
came to pass. The day after the crowning of the
Queen, the King was stabbed to death by an insane
man. The news of the horror whirled through Paris
and beyond to the gardens of the deposed Marguerite
of Valois.

When, on the day of this horrible deed, Monsieur

Vincent came to Queen Marguerite's palace the wonted gay life was hushed. Only a few courtiers stood in the anterooms, as though waiting for the latest reports.

Queen Marguerite had withdrawn to the inner apartments of the palace. Did she mourn for him who had deposed, repudiated her? Was she stunned by the murder which had again touched her life, as so often in that bloody St. Bartholomew's night?

When Monsieur Vincent approached the Queen's secretary, Monsieur du Fresne, to deliver a number of reports, an aged savant came to the almoner, placed a hand on his shoulder and looked into his eyes with unsteady glances.

Monsieur Vincent was perturbed. Did not this man have a fever?

"What says Monsieur Vincent," began the learned man, "concerning the course of events? Of course, Monsieur does not know that I am a theologian of the Sorbonne and have been teaching these many years: There is a God and this we prove by logical conclusions. One of these logical conclusions is that there must be a God to account for the wisdom with which the universe is governed.

"Understand me correctly, Monsieur Vincent!" continued the savant looking about as though wishing to be sure that nobody was eavesdropping. Then he grasped Vincent de Paul under the arm and drew him closer, as if to speak confidentially. He whispered into the young priest's ear:

"Does Monsieur Vincent say there is a God?"

Vincent gazed at the learned man, whose eyes betrayed insanity.

"Come, come, Monsieur," urged the theologian of the Sorbonne, and led the Queen's almoner out into the garden, to a silent, secluded grove.

"Of the King they say," he now began to tell Vincent, "yes, of the King they say that before the altar in Saint-Denis he renounced the creed of the Huguenots to which he had clung, and accepted the Catholic faith. Why, think you, Monsieur Vincent, why did he do that? Because he had come to realize the errors of the Huguenots and wished to return to the true faith? Why, Monsieur Vincent, did this revelation come to the King, whom a madman has now stretched on his bier; why, Monsieur, did this revelation come to him only in the hour when the throne of France was to be won, but the price was acknowledgment by the Catholic people of France and by the Pope of Rome? The King, the fourth Henry, is reported to have said: 'Very well, I will foreswear the faith of my youth, the faith of the Huguenots, for which I have wielded my sword many times! I shall be a Catholic, for it seems to me that the throne of France is worth a Catholic Mass.'

"Does a God in Heaven rule this world, or does greed rule it, Monsieur? . . . Greed for thrones and benefices? I am a professor of theology. The old traditional books tell me I must teach that God rules the world. Am I a truthful and a wise teacher, Monsieur, or a concoctor of poisons, a maker of lies? Because when I look at the world and ask my intelligence who rules it, I find no God, but only greed, on the part of kings and noblemen, cardinals and prelates, abbots, all clerics in general. Who rules the world?

"Years ago, Monsieur, I begged permission not to have to pray the Breviary, day after day recite the holy Psalms. What place have the sacred words in my mouth the while my eyes look upon the lies of the world? Otherwise the foulness would be in my mouth, too. I shall no longer lie about the world. But that was the beginning only, Monsieur Vincent. I confess to you, I can scarcely manage to pray the Our Father. Not even the very first words, 'Our Father' — who is our Father, where is He who directs these evils? As long as I have lived and studied in the world, the people of France have been strangling each other, for their religion's sake, they say, and the shepherds, whom God sent into the world, the bishops and priests, chase after nothing but benefices.

"The ship of the Church is a wreck on a stormy sea and those whose duty it is to guide and lead, they abandon it to the raging current of the times and shrug their shoulders, asking, What can we do? Wolves came into the land. I see nothing but wolves, Monsieur Vincent, each one seeking to tear the other to pieces and live on the other's flesh.

"But the most horrible of all, Monsieur Vincent,

is this — they demand that I read Mass. Shall I raise the circle of unleavened bread in my hands and utter the words over it and believe and then show the host to the people so they will kneel before it and strike their breasts and believe that in my hands I hold the Bread of Angels, the Body of the Son of God, and that he who eats of this Bread with divine desire sits at the table of our Lord's supper? I know nothing more terrible than that moment, Monsieur. How were it possible that this miracle of change could take place in my fingers and I nothing but a wolf, a worthless wretch, a madman? In such moments I am tempted not to speak the words, to crush the disk of unleavened bread and throw it at the feet of the people, to trample it underfoot and to cry out: 'It is all a lie, see, see, we merely make believe, to entangle you in lies, to bring you to your knees, to make you fold your hands; for if you do that, you brothers and sisters, and have your hands devoutly folded and are gazing toward me with reverence, then those who are in league with me without your knowing it can easily get into your pockets and take your money.'

"I must escape from this morass of hellish lies. No more 'Our Fathers,' for there is no Father; no Masses — no Consecration, for it is witchcraft, deception, and betrayal before all the people. And I shall teach them that nothing rules the world but devilish greed, and no matter where you go, you will find no God, no angels, but only thieves, robbers, murderers!

"The soldier, Monsieur Vincent, can live only with honor, the priest only if he has the respect of the people and of himself. The soldier no longer has any honor, the priest no longer any respect; and I, Monsieur Vincent, I have no longer any faith! Men have taken it away from me!"

He clung to Vincent. It was evening. The two walked in the Queen's garden and darkness began to fall.

Vincent had listened to the feverish recital without saying a word of disagreement, had let the man speak to the end. As they walked along he pressed the savant's hand occasionally.

The poor professor of the Sorbonne clung to Vincent and pleaded:"Now night is coming, Brother Vincent, do not let me alone!"

Queen Marguerite's almoner led the other through the streets of Saint-Germain to the house in which he lived with several other priests of Monsieur de Bérulle's circle. He took the despairing one to his room, pressed him to sit in a chair to rest, sought out a bit of bread and a little water. He had nothing more to give his guest for supper.

The man of sick mind stared a while, took the bread and when he broke it, smiled a little. Then the rigidity began to lessen, but gave way only to an unnatural tremor that shook his whole body.

"See, Monsieur Vincent," he laughed unhappily, "we theologians of the Sorbonne are expected to teach the whole people that Christ the Son of God came down to earth and suffered His terrible Passion and death to redeem men. That is what He is supposed to have done.

"Where will I find even one man who sees me in my misery and will come to me and say, 'I will take your anguish from you, I will take it from you!' Did Christ the Lord take it from us? If He had taken it from us, it would no longer be here! But it is still here!"

He laughed once more and with shaking hand took hold of the glass and spilled the water on the table and on his coat and what remained in the goblet he drank. Then he set it heavily back on the table. He braced himself on the chair, rose to his feet and went to the window. There he stood, shaking.

"It is the night!" he said.

At this moment one of the priests in the house, whose room was under that of Monsieur Vincent, began to sing. He sang the song of St. John of the Cross, a song he had learned to love, and its title is "The Dark Night of the Soul." And thus he began:

"Upon an obscure night
Fevered with love in love's anxiety
(O hapless-happy plight!)
I went, none seeing me,
Forth from my house where all things quiet be."

Monsieur Vincent knew well that words alone could not cure this sick man, that nothing less than tender, enveloping love and pity could save him, so he came close to the miserable man of learning and asked, "Do you know the song of the soul's dark night?"

The other nodded, yes, yes. "From the dark body in which our soul is imprisoned she fares forth, from her hut into the night of the valley, upward to the mount, where the morning rays of the sun strike earliest."

And Vincent went on. "There the soul will meet her bridegroom, the Lord Jesus Christ."

The priest in the room below continued his song:

"Blest night of wandering,
In secret, where by none might I be spied,
Nor I see anything;
Without a light or guide,
Save that which in my heart burnt in my side."

"There is nothing to do in this night but to follow faith, my brother of the Sorbonne. Faith is for us like a stone of heaviness, and when it plunges into the abyss it sinks straight into the arms of God!"

Below is the song of the soul seeking her bridegroom:

"That light did lead me on,
More surely than the shining of noontide,
Where well I knew that one
Did for my coming bide;
Where He abode may none but He abide.

"O night that didst lead thus,
O night more lovely than the dawn of light,
O night that broughtest us,
Lover to lover's sight,
Lover with loved in marriage of delight!"

Suddenly the learned man screamed in the night.

"Does He come, the bridegroom of our soul? Is He here — will He disclose His nearness to us? If He does not come, I shall go in search of Him! What say you, Monsieur Vincent? I remember your words about the stone that is heavy and if it plunge, plunges straight into the arms of God!"

In a fiercely wild motion the sick man sprang to the window, would have hurled himself through it, down to the ground beneath.

For a moment Vincent was helpless with fear and surprise. Then he grasped the madman and pulled him back from the window.

"What are you doing? — For God's sake!"

Instantly the man's frenzy vanished, he let himself be helped to the bed by Vincent and sank upon it. He lay there with closed eyes, exhausted. Only the lips twitched, but no words came forth. Only once he cried out "Who will take this agony from me?" followed by the intense silence of the night.

Up from the room below came the priest's voice, singing the great Spanish mystic's song, telling how the soul invites to the feast of love the hills and meadows, glens and cliffs, the distant islands of the sea, the fragrance of all flowers, the booming of the surf, the gentle murmur of the wind. And how the soul surrenders all things to the service of the Bridegroom. She has aught else to do now, naught but to love Him. With a bitter smile, the sick man repeated the final words. "I have naught else to do now, naught but to love Him!" It was a final encouragement.

Now Monsieur Vincent, sitting beside the man, bowed his head and prayed. Once the learned one opened his eyes and looked at the young priest. What was he praying? Then he closed his eyes again, and listened.

Vincent de Paul spoke softly, but with intensity. "O God in Heaven, merciful God, have pity on this poor man; save him, Lord, accept me as a sacrifice for him.

"The clouds that darken his soul do Thou drive from the valley in which he dwells, let them come upon me. In my room, O Lord, there is ample space. Drive out the devils that are destroying his house and tell them to come and live here with me, but save him!

"Take from his shoulders the burden they carry, put it on my shoulders. I offer myself to Thee so that he may once more believe. For him, too, Christ the Lord suffered the death of sacrifice."

From the bed came a soft weeping.

Vincent had risen and gone to the window. He gazed out into the night. Then until morning he knelt near the bed of the learned man.

As morning neared, Vincent saw how his guest arose, arranged his clothes, prepared to leave. The host arose from his knees and compelled the savant to remain. He left the room to order breakfast.

"I have slept well," said the Sorbonne professor. "I

am still somewhat tired. However, I must have had
evil experiences during the night. I thank you. It lies
behind me like an evil dream, which has plagued me
for years. I have gone to the window several times to
plunge myself down — and now, all at once it is gone!
How did it happen?

"Yesterday I saw the world full of foulness and every
evil, today I see it filled with God's wonders. It probably was due to my eyes. If one's eyes are diseased, they
see disease everywhere; if well, all things seem well.
What did you do to me this night, Monsieur Vincent?
I do not know, but whatever it was, I thank you. I believe that you have saved me."

Then he took leave of his host. At the door he
turned to say, "May God preserve you, Monsieur Vincent, from ever suffering the anguish of doubt! It is
the worst hell there can be on earth!"

When the theologian had gone, Vincent must per-
force think how he had offered himself to God, offered
to assume the agony of this man. He tried to banish
the thought, but it proved too strong and persistent.
He was compelled to ask himself whether he had ever
doubted God. How had such a senseless notion occurred to him? He wished to pray. But when he began,
"Our Father," he was shaken. He could not go on,
could not keep from dwelling on his experiences of the
night, on all the horrible things the sick man had revealed. Thus Vincent sat there, compelled to think on
these matters.

And when he went to the chapel of the house to read Mass and the moment of Consecration neared, a tremendous fear gripped him. He could not speak the words that cause the Great Change! He did as on all other mornings, bowed low above the bread, but his lips remained dumb, and he consumed the unconsecrated bread.

This day, one of his confreres sought him out in his room, and finding him deep in thought, asked: "What is it, Monsieur Vincent?"

To this he answered: "Had I known what it means to be a priest, I would never have dared! In the sight of Heaven I say, I should never have dared to become a priest!"

But then he roused himself, stood up and crossed the street to the Charité, sat beside the beds of the sick. There the agonizing thoughts left him, and there only.

As soon as Vincent left the hospital and was alone again, the terrible experiences of the previous night flooded his soul. He heard the words of the insane man; they shattered everything, tore his faith to pieces.

In the solitude of his room he grabbed a piece of parchment and wrote on it: "I believe! — I believe! — I believe!" Wrote it and shoved the piece of parchment through his clothes onto his breast, so it lay on his heart.

Those who knew Monsieur Vincent wondered at the change that had come over him. His glance was unsteady. He walked about for hours in the meadows of Saint-Germain, until he reached the crest of a hill and standing there looked out over the land and fell into deep thought, until he remembered how he had come to the place. Then he stammered like a desperate man, "I believe!"

He went to see Pierre de Bérulle. This priest looked upon him as a physician looks upon one who is sick, put his hand on Vincent's shoulder, but said only this:

"You had better go to the Charité, Monsieur Vincent."

Vincent nodded assent. Only with the sick did he find surcease.

Thus he suffered for two years, and one night he knew immeasurable misery. He had that evening, in the court of the house where he lived with Monsieur de Bérulle, encountered the theologian of the Sorbonne, for the first time since the night of the savant's desperate anguish and the song of the soul's dark night. The learned man sat in a circle of priests and seemed fully recovered. He glanced up at Vincent with a sunny smile, and the memory even of that sinister night seemed to have faded from his mind. Instead, all the anguished fear and desperate grief were now in Vincent's soul.

In the loneliness of the night Vincent realized that now he, too, was being assailed by madness. He sought a piece of bread, he poured water into a glass, and suddenly he was convulsed with terror as he sat at the table. He sat now as the learned man had sat at this table, and his despair was the same. Here he broke the bread. Here he spoke the same blasphemous words that had come from the other's mouth. Avidly he grasped the goblet, spilled the water as the other had spilled it, and an impulse which he could not understand drove him to the window, to plunge through it.

And then he heard his own words, " — and if you plunge into the abyss, you will fall straight into the arms of God!"

Already he was at the window ledge —

Out of the night came a song. Was he dreaming, or was one of the priests really singing of the soul's yearning for her Bridegroom?

> "When, O my God, shall I be set on fire
> With Thy sweet love's enkindling?
> When shall I enter in at last to joy?
> Or when be offered
> Wholly upon love's altar and consumed?"

All of the sweet songs of St. John of the Cross, which he had heard so often, sounded now in his ears. He heard again the rapturous lines:

> "O night that didst lead thus,
> O night more lovely than the dawn of light,
> O night that broughtest us,
> Lover to lover's sight,
> Lover with loved in marriage of delight!"

And he heard finally how the soul cries out that now

it has naught else to do in life, naught but to love
Him, her Bridegroom!

He staggered back into the room, dragged himself
to the bed and fell upon it.

The other had gone the same way. Who had led the
other, now him?

As he lay there, despair took hold of him for the last
time and he cried out,

"Lord God, if Thou wilt take all doubts from my
heart and if the evil spirits do not torture me to death,
I shall henceforth seek none but the tormented ones
of earth, and go to them as Thy humble servant — to
the hungry and give them Thy bread, to the naked
and clothe them in Thy garment, to the imprisoned,
to release them from the captivity of earth and lead
them to the freedom of Thy kingdom. This I swear to
Thee I will do until I die!"

There came upon him then an intense hunger for
the Bread of Angels, and in his ear the song sounded
again: "The dark night of the soul!"

He felt how an arm of divine mercy embraced him
in his sleep. His hand came slowly to lay over his heart.
There he heard the crackle of the piece of parchment
on which he had written: "I believe — believe —
believe!"

He sang in his heart the words of the song, the soul's
glad cry: Now there is naught for me in all the world,
naught in life and in eternity but to love my Bridegroom, Christ the Lord!

Then faintness overpowered him.

The next morning Monsieur Vincent awoke and was well. Tired still because of the ordeal, he sat at the table and broke bread. Leaving his room, he went to the Charité, and those who saw him marveled, for the shifty glance of his eyes had given place to a look steady and serene.

Vincent, a tired but convalescent man, gazed about in wonderment, for it seemed to him that he had only passed through a deep dream.

Chapter VIII

STEWARD OF THE GOODS OF GOD

IN THOSE days there came to Monsieur Vincent a priest from Dax, near his native Pouy, bringing with him the greetings of his family. And then the visitor began to tell Vincent a tale of misery.

How badly they fared, Vincent's mother and brothers and sisters!

"They have their daily bread?" asked Vincent.

"Yes," said the priest, "that they have. But how they must toil for it, day after day, and how careful they were and how much they denied themselves so that one of the sons might give himself to study and become a priest and win a benefice! Now they have a son and brother who is in Paris and is almoner to Queen Marguerite and has an abbacy with generous revenues . . ."

"Do they say that?" demanded Vincent.

"No, they do not say it, but I saw that they must think such thoughts. You know that in Pouy there is another family and that they, too, had a hard life. But one of their sons studied and became a priest and then an abbot. How generously he provided for his father and his mother, and all his brothers and sisters! He raised all of them to quite easy circumstances. The

people at Pouy say, Vincent, that the example of this
family prompted your father, years ago, to send you to
school, because he hoped by that means to provide for
himself and his family. Do you know this?"

"I know full well that my father planned it so, and
by Heaven! I myself often thought as he did," answered Vincent. "But tell me, is that other family
happier, now that they have reached affluence by
means of Church revenues?"

The priest from Dax was embarrassed. "They
squandered it," he admitted, "couldn't keep anything
together."

"And are they not more miserable now than
before?"

"Certainly," the other confessed. "The abbot died
and another was given the living and the family at
Pouy was plunged into extreme need. I admit that.
But at least they had some good years."

"They had some years of sin, not good years!" declared Vincent. "And now they are more miserable
than ever. When you go back to Pouy and to my
mother and the others and you hear any of them speak
a complaining word, tell them I send them nothing
because I have nothing; and because I wish to save
them from the fate of that other family, which they
have seen. What is given to me I do not own. I am the
almoner of the Lord Jesus Christ and must give an
account of all that is placed in my hands.

"But those who misuse the goods of the Church in-

stead of spending it for the works which our Lord
bade us do, feed the hungry, clothe the naked, visit the
sick — all who refuse to serve Him in this way, will be
ruined. They fill their hearts with rottenness, for that
is what earthly riches are. May God keep me and mine
from such a misfortune!"

Vincent de Paul arose and asked his visitor: "Will
you go with me? I am going to one of the poor quarters
of Paris."

The priest from Dax had risen, too. "I am sorry, I
have not the time to go with you. I have business to
attend to and tomorrow I must leave Paris."

Chapter IX

CLICHY'S WONDER WEEKS

MONSIEUR VINCENT was now thirty years of age. He asked Monsieur de Bérulle to admit him into the group called the Oratory of Our Lord Jesus Christ, which de Bérulle had organized in Paris the year before, in 1611. Some years previous to this Monsieur de Bérulle had gathered a small number of diocesan priests to form a shock troop which would undertake to reconquer for Christ's kingdom the unhappy land of France, which seemed almost lost to the Church, for it was apparent that the chief cause of the country's sad condition was the lack of good priests. At a Church council held at this time, the Pope himself had declared that the evils of the day were traceable to bad priests. Wolves had fallen upon the flock. The priestly office was not filled by worthy men who spent themselves with zeal for the House of the Lord. There prevailed the frivolous custom which permitted families of the nobility to provide for their younger sons by foisting them upon the Church in bishoprics and abbacies, even into the office of simple priests, merely for the sake of the benefices and the revenues to be gained.

And the holy life of the priesthood had broken down.

But from the midst of these deplorable conditions, divine grace produced saintly men who appeared suddenly and by the glowing love with which they devoted themselves to the people who had strayed, proved to be true disciples of Jesus. One of these shining exemplars was Pierre de Bérulle.

Monsieur Vincent desired to place his life in the hands of Monsieur de Bérulle and asked permission to submit himself wholly to the founder of the Oratory as his spiritual director.

The priests of this new Oratory of Our Lord Jesus Christ, which de Bérulle had organized in imitation of St. Philip Neri, remained diocesan priests. They took no vows such as monks take, or the mendicant friars, but lived a community life, the better to walk in the path of spiritual progress and discuss and act in common concerning their supremely important work. They felt that when they had schooled themselves in the spiritual life they would be better qualified to undertake the cure of souls among the people.

Monsieur de Bérulle had been Vincent's spiritual director for two years, but had not admitted the Queen's almoner to complete membership in the Oratory. As often as Vincent begged for this, Monsieur de Bérulle shook his head. It was not because he did not consider Vincent de Paul worthy, but because he deemed him destined for another kind of life.

Vincent's soul was troubled. To be sure, as almoner

of Queen Marguerite he could traverse the poorest districts of Paris and do good to many. He was animated, however, by an intense desire to do more than meet the physical needs of the sick and poor, for he saw clearly that the healthy and the rich needed spiritual help much more than did the poor and the sick.

At this time there came to the house of the Oratorians the sad-hearted parish priest of Clichy, to tell Monsieur de Bérulle that he could no longer administer his charge, that the task was more than he could do. The little church was in ruins and its collapse was a symbol of the lives of his people. So the Clichy parish priest, whose name was Monsieur Bourgoing, begged to be admitted into the Oratory and that a successor take his place at Clichy.

Now Monsieur Vincent came to speak with Monsieur de Bérulle. The founder of the Oratory received him smilingly and said to him, "Monsieur Vincent, since you insist upon carrying more worries than you are already bearing, I as your spiritual director command you to go at once to Clichy and assume the pastorate of its parish."

Everything had been arranged, and the next morning the Bishop's notary, Monsieur Thomas Galbot, would await Monsieur Vincent at the church in Clichy.

Vincent de Paul was dumbfounded and deeply moved by the suddenness of this command. He bowed his head in humble acquiescence and hurried to Monsieur du Fresne, the private secretary of Marguerite of

Valois, to tell him of being given a new assignment.

The next morning at the appointed hour Monsieur Vincent arrived at Clichy, a small place in the suburbs of Paris. Simple peasant farmers lived there, toiling in the sweat of their brows to wring a livelihood from the planted acres and the meadows. But Clichy was also a place of costly and pompous country homes in contrast to the humble dwellings of the peasants. Rich men of Paris had their week-end villas there, to which they resorted during the summer or when they had hours of leisure away from their affairs in the city. Even from a distance Monsieur Vincent saw how dilapidated the little church was!

The peasants, having learned that a new priest was coming, had gathered in front of the church in groups, filled with curiosity.

Monsieur Vincent walked toward the door. There was the Bishop's notary, who conveyed to him a document, given to the notary by Monsieur de Bérulle, in which the Archbishop of Paris authorized the priest Vincent de Paul to administer the parish.

Thereupon the new pastor requested the key of the church and was presented with it by Monsieur Galbot, the notary. Then Vincent entered, threw himself on the floor before the altar and kissed the dust of the sacred place. He arose, kissed the altar and the missal, touched the tabernacle and the baptismal font with his fingers as indicative of taking possession, and mounted the pulpit.

The people of Clichy, the humble peasants, heard their new curé's first sermon with amazement. How strange his words! He spoke of the reverence due this place, which seemed to have been profaned, and of their own bodies and souls as the vessels and the dwelling places of the Most High, vessels and dwelling places over which the weeds of evil had grown wild.

Then he offered up the Holy Sacrifice and the people marveled at the deep reverence and absorbed devotion with which he read the Mass, and they returned to their homes full of wonder.

Through the years they had toiled in their homes and in the fields and had often grown angry at the frivolous lives of the rich. To be sure, they had had a little church and a parish priest, but the curé himself had grown too tired to concern himself with the sheep of his flock, who had strayed in all directions and had almost forgotten that they had a shepherd in their midst.

Now they became aware that the new priest, Monsieur Vincent, penetrated every street, every lane, entered every house to visit his spiritual children, to learn to know them, to talk with them about their condition, about the humdrum affairs of their simple lives. And they noticed that to the houses where there were sick people, he went every day.

He went to the homes of the rich, too. They were astonished when their servants announced that the new parish priest was waiting to pay his respects to the master and the mistress. What did he want? At first they did not wish to receive him, but did so anyhow out of courtesy. They found him to be a priest distinguished by courteous demeanor and noble character who discussed the needs of the parish with them in a serious but friendly fashion.

A parish? What was that?

What? — It was their concern, too, the common welfare?

There were poor people in Clichy who might well be scandalized and angered by the easy lives and extravagance of the rich?

He wished then to beg, the young priest? No, he wished nothing for his sack. No, he bade the noble lady, the rich lord themselves to carry their alms to the poor — and he felt sure that if they but saw what suffering and dire need there were a few steps from their houses, they would give themselves to the care of the poor and sick.

Everybody began to take notice and soon realized that something new had been brought to Clichy by Monsieur Vincent.

The next Sunday the church was crowded with those who had come out of curiosity and who became aware, with wonder and as from afar, of the ardor of the prayers and songs which their fathers had heard, their fathers centuries ago. Those who built Notre Dame of Paris, they must have had such intense faith, **such serene hope, such burning love in their hearts.**

It was gossiped about that the new curé had gone to the houses of those who lived in enmity, to melt their hearts with his stirring words and restore peace. Why, he went even to the homes of the Huguenots! And spoke to them as to friends! For how many years had the Catholics and the Huguenots striven to kill each other, and the leaders of the two parties had whipped their followers into making murderous attacks! And now came one who preached that the old conflict was the work of Hell, not of Christ's kingdom! Never again dared the Catholics hate the Huguenots. A monstrous crime and a Satanic deed it had been, its infamy coming down to the present hour, thus he spoke of the massacre of St. Bartholomew's Day. Now the task was to restore the kingdom of the Lord Jesus Christ in truth. His kingdom, however, is one of love and kindness.

The rich began to give of their abundance to the poor and sick. Stolen goods were returned to their owners. Money was placed secretly at Monsieur Vincent's window, with notes asking him to spend it in restoring the ruined church. Or, that it be given back to the one from whom it was stolen. That a school be established to train twelve boys to become priests in the spirit of Monsieur Vincent.

A few weeks had passed, no more, and there came to Clichy a learned priest of the Sorbonne, at the invitation of Monsieur Vincent, to preach at his request to the people of his parish.

But when the learned priest returned to Paris, dumbfounded, as if shortly awakened from a dream, he related to his astonished hearers what it was that had impressed him so sharply and deeply: The people of Clichy live like a congregation of angels!

One year had passed, the second had begun when Monsieur Vincent received from his spiritual director the command to leave Clichy and come back to Paris. He had done his work so well that a vicar could now be entrusted with the pastoral duties.

Bewildered by the suddenness of the summons, but obedient, Vincent de Paul left the little village which had become a home to him. When he said farewell he saw many eyes filled with grief and the hands which were stretched out to him trembled.

He himself wept. He would remain Clichy's parish priest, he told the people. Only temporarily would a vicar take his place. But he did not know for what work Monsieur de Bérulle had selected him.

Chapter X

A Countess and Her Vassals

IT WAS the evening of January 25 in the year 1613 when Monsieur Vincent with his few simple belongings returned to Paris.

When he had welcomed him affectionately, Monsieur de Bérulle revealed that he had chosen him for a task for which none but he was qualified.

The task was the education of the three sons of the Count and Countess de Gondi, members of one of the most powerful families in Paris.

The Gondi were Florentines, not even of noble lineage. Their cradle had been a miller's home in Tuscany, whence one of them came to France and by the favor of fortune had risen swiftly. He succeeded in winning a title of nobility and one of his descendants, Albert de Gondi-Retz, had been the favorite and privy counselor of King Charles IX.

Being foreigners, the Gondi were more hated than loved by the nobles of France. They possessed Florentine cunning, adaptable court manners, were secretive and subtle, and while they shone brilliantly in the eyes of the world, particularly of the mob, they were capable of the foulest deeds.

Thus they succeeded readily in gaining powerful influence at the French court and playing important roles, for this court cared for naught but to increase the power of the King to such an extent that he seemed to be almost a god, and any sort of deception and ruthlessness seemed justified if it but served to enhance the outward glory of the French throne.

One of the means employed by the kings of France toward this end was to control not only all State offices but also those of the Church. Among the people there was current the saying of King Henry IV, the former Huguenot who returned to the Catholic faith in order to gain the crown: The throne of France is worth a Catholic Mass.

The French kings had managed, by means of a pact with the Pope, a concordat it was called, to gain the power of filling all bishoprics. Thus it was that in Paris the Gondi family attained to high positions, which were practically inherited from father to son. The first-born Gondi was traditionally General of the Royal Galleys; the second-born, Archbishop of Paris.

When Monsieur Vincent heard the name Gondi he was frightened. Before the eyes of his spirit he saw Albert de Gondi-Retz, the favorite of Charles IX, of whom he knew that he had been one of the leading atheists of his time. Splendid as a Florentine dagger outwardly, he had been treacherous. The method he employed was called by those who knew it, the serpentine way of the Gondi.

In that sinister hour in which the Queen Mother and three conspirators had gone to the young King to persuade him to order the St. Bartholomew's massacre, a Gondi, this Albert de Gondi-Retz, had been one of the three.

And now Monsieur Vincent was asked to enter, not the house of this man, but the house of his eldest son, Emmanuel.

"You must not be frightened, Monsieur Vincent," explained de Bérulle. "Emmanuel de Gondi, Commander of the Galleys, does not go the serpentine way of his father. In his heart there is a pure, deep love of his fellow men. He cherishes virtue and strives to do works of goodness. It is another of the miracles which always astonish us anew, Monsieur Vincent, when God causes a tree of virtue to spring up in the midst of vice. Emmanuel de Gondi seeks the land of the just and of the perfect, and asks a helmsman for his ship. Do you wish to refuse?

"At Count Emmanuel's side is his wife, Francoise Marguerite de Silly. She is a true *grande dame* by birth, at once immensely rich and deeply pious. You must know that she holds all earthly things to be mere delusion, vanity. She feels uncertain in the world, is troubled with fear lest she miss the goal of perfection, and she knows that one of her sons, Pierre de Gondi, will be a peer of France, and the second son, Jean Paul, eventually Archbishop of Paris.

"As yet Jean Paul de Gondi is a boy, but it seems

to me," added Monsieur de Bérulle, "the virtues of
his father are mixed in him with the vices of Albert
de Gondi, his grandfather. There are roses and poisonous plants in the garden of life. The boy may honor
virtue and religion, he may some time do them fierce,
sudden violence. A man may be keen-minded, but
intellect alone will not keep him from being a knave,
feared by the nobles and at court; because of his
brilliant person and because of his ambiguous words
he is an idol of the mob. Perhaps he will be the leader
of rebellions. And on the same day on which he
wields the sword he will go to Notre Dame to preach
to the people.

"His mother gave him a Breviary, because he is
destined for the priesthood. But when she emptied
his pockets, where the Breviary ought to have been
she found instead a Florentine dagger. Weeping, she
came to me. He is still, as I have said, a boy, but
already he speaks Latin like Tacitus. The elegance of
his French even now surpasses that of the foremost
writers. Perhaps coming generations will know him as
the most restless of France's nobles. What fate may
befall the people through this Archbishop of Paris!"

Monsieur Vincent had listened, much troubled,
and looked wholly discouraged.

"I must not forget the third of the boys," said
Monsieur de Bérulle then, and smiled. "Henri, the
youngest. You will find him a lad like an angel.
However, he is delicate and I believe and fear that

he will be an early perfected one. You will love him and he will be a consolation to you and give you strength to endure the violent Jean Paul close to you."

That evening Monsieur Vincent betook himself to the palace of the Gondi, in obedience to his spiritual director. The world of the great flowed through the halls and rooms of this residence, almost more luxuriantly, more elegantly than in the palace of the Queen.

The Countess, a tender, generous woman about as old as Vincent, received him. "I beg you, Monsieur Vincent, make saints out of my children!"

He looked at her for a moment and saw that her soul was deeply troubled.

"I believe, Monsieur Vincent" — and now she bowed her head, so he could not read what was in her eyes — "that the world is filled with vanity, disappointment. We are like a people wandering in a mist. There are many educators who deceive the young with treacherous, bright goals. I should like to preserve my children from the brutal errors of life that would cause them to hold outward glory and power and riches more desirable than virtue."

She gave him her hands and he felt how they trembled. He became aware in that moment how much this woman feared that she and those she loved might miss the true goal of life.

Vincent was given a room in the midst of the big palace's tumultuous life. To this room he withdrew for many hours of solitude, as if he wished to acquire certainty for himself in this task through prayer.

He appeared before the Count and Countess only when they summoned him. He devoted himself to the education of the children.

However, he was summoned often by the Countess to accompany her; for no day passed on which she did not visit the poor and the sick. Monsieur Vincent was to learn in this way her desire to do good, that he might accomplish it where she herself could not penetrate. And she begged him also, because she trusted his eyes more than her own, to show her constantly new ways of helping others.

At first Monsieur Vincent had remained almost hidden amid the large number of servants in the palace. Scarcely did the servants know that a new tutor had arrived, so well did he withdraw himself. But let a servant become ill and stay abed in his room, soon there would be a knock at the door and Monsieur Vincent would enter, seat himself beside the sick one and talk with him.

And when rancor broke out between two servants and they met each other with angry looks, Vincent noticed this before anyone else and in the evening, when the servants were resting, he went to the quarters of the enemies and reconciled them.

At the request of the Countess, Monsieur Vincent gave the house a daily routine to which all the servants were subject, and Count and Countess de Gondi themselves followed it.

In this manner, life in the palace began to assume a clear, orderly character and a definite plan appeared in the charitable work of the Countess.

There prevailed at this time among the nobles of France the vicious custom of challenging to duels even upon slight provocation and no matter how the quarrel may have arisen. The tendency to personal combat has been in the hearts of men since ancient days. Even when an accusation was brought against a woman, the accuser was wont to bolster his charge by challenging all who set themselves up as defenders of the woman. They believed that God would intervene and that the outcome of the duel would reveal innocence or guilt. If a man undertook to defend the accused but his swordsmanship proved less skillful than that of his opponent and the defender fell, the innocent woman was considered guilty and judged accordingly.

Now during the forty years of warfare with the Huguenots, every French nobleman had engaged in such combats almost every day, and many who felt themselves useless in the peaceful time that had suddenly come upon the land, began to seek opportunities for duels, which became a passion with them.

In vain did the Church place her ban on this brutal custom and kings of France issue decrees against its excesses.

One day a servant, coming secretly to his room, gave Monsieur Vincent a report which troubled the priest exceedingly and throughout the night he was troubled.

It was the next morning. Each day in the Gondi residence began with Holy Mass celebrated by Monsieur Vincent in the palace chapel. The Count and Countess and their children assisted at the Holy Sacrifice; and all the servants, too.

On this morning, when the Mass had been offered up and all were waiting for Count Emmanuel to arise from his prie-dieu near the altar and walk out of the chapel, he turned about and gave a signal to the servants to go. He nodded then to the Countess and she and their children left. The Count wished to be alone, wholly alone for prayer. They knew that he would start on a journey that evening. Perhaps he wished to beg Heaven's blessing on an important new enterprise. Thus they thought and went humbly from the chapel, a final prayer on their lips.

For a long time Count de Gondi knelt absorbed. When he looked up he saw Monsieur Vincent prostrate before the altar, his arms extended as if nailed to a cross. Until now the Count had believed himself alone. And as if he had read this in the Count's glance, Vincent arose, made a genuflection in front of the altar, and was about to leave. But there was something so unusual in every movement of the priest that de Gondi followed them intently. Then Monsieur Vincent turned about and came close to the Count's kneeling bench.

For a moment the glances of the two men met.

The priest bowed his head humbly and sank to his knees before the Count and in that position spoke.

"Monsieur le General, I have learned from a trustworthy source that because of a serious insult, you will this night engage in a duel. I come to you in the Name of the Lord Jesus Christ, whose Body you saw in my hands a short time ago and whom you have been worshiping. In His Name I come to tell you that you and your whole house will be struck by the curse of Heaven if you do not instantly decide not to commit this crime."

Count de Gondi stared at the bold man kneeling before him, who now arose and without another word turned toward the altar, bent his knee again in homage to the Blessed Sacrament and quietly withdrew.

For an instant the shame of having been reprimanded stung the General and it seemed to him he must stand up and rebuke the priest and put him back in the category of servant. However, he admitted that he had been prepared to forsake the boundaries of the kingdom of Christ. His head sank heavily upon his arms and he gripped the prie-dieu with tense fingers. The satin cushion with silver fringes slid from under his knees and he felt the hard wood of penance.

After some time de Gondi arose, ready to settle the quarrel in the spirit of his Lord Jesus Christ, to whose banner he had sworn loyal allegiance.

Now the Gondi family possessed large estates in various parts of the land. For weeks, months even, the General and his family lived in one or the other of their castles out on the flat acres of an estate. The Countess loved best of all then to go through the villages, visit the homes of the peasants, inquire into their needs, and administer justice, investigating especially to ascertain whether magistrates on the estates dealt honestly, and with mildness, for nothing saddened her more than complaints of oppression and of justice perverted.

In the several parts of the family domain there always awaited the kindly Countess every peasant who was in need, who had suffered an injury. Often she would sit on the rude benches in peasant homes while her vassals humbly approached. Surrounded by her manservants and maidservants, she promised at once to help the sick, she commanded a servant to summon the judge against whom complaints were made, she herself arbitrated the petty quarrels of the peasants, as well as enmities of years' standing. Monsieur Vincent stood beside her and in all she did, she awaited his counsel before acting.

One day in January, 1617, when the Gondi were at their castle of Folleville near Amiens in Picardy, a messenger came from the village of Gannes, imploring Monsieur Vincent to hasten to the bedside of a dying man. The distance was about two hours' walk. The name of the dying villager was reported to the Countess and as she held him to be an exceptionally upright man and had known him for many years, she was filled with compassion and decided to accompany Monsieur Vincent on this sick call.

The priest was to visit the man first and prepare him for death. Meanwhile the Countess would visit the poor in the village, then come to the home of the dying man, to show him her esteem and her sympathy.

Monsieur Vincent had begun to hear the confession of the old man and was speaking gently with him. He saw suddenly that the man's eyes betrayed a sorely troubled soul.

"You will live only a few more hours perhaps, and then you will appear before your Maker. We are now preparing you, clothing you for your appearance before the eternal throne. When you confess your sins in the Sacrament of Penance we remove from your soul all the stains which have fallen on your garment. What you sinned in previous years was probably forgiven in previous confessions and absolutions. But your appearance will be the more pleasing to God if you confess them once again and resolve to include all the sins of your whole life in this, your last confession. So let us review your life once more from the beginning to this hour."

When Monsieur Vincent spoke thus, he saw how the peasant was startled. The dying man raised his hands, as if to ward off the priest's request. But Vincent de Paul took the peasant's hands in his and held them fast and spoke consoling words of confidence.

"What you disclosed to a priest in the past you will surely be able to disclose to me now; the same wounds of the soul, so that they may be forever healed."

But the eyes of the dying man betrayed increasing fear and his whole body trembled, so that Vincent took the poor fellow into his arms, he was so near to fainting.

"Did you perhaps conceal something in one of your confessions?"

Then it came chokingly, in agitated breath. The peasant clung desperately to Monsieur Vincent, as though he feared to plunge into the abyss. And the secret of his life was revealed.

When, after a while, the Countess came with goodness and pity to the bedside, the old man lay quiet and transfigured on the straw.

"You are not afraid of death, are you?" asked the Countess. "You have lived a good life and all who know you have looked up to you with esteem. So you do not need to be afraid to die."

"No," said the man, "now I do not need to fear death. I thank you for rescuing me through Monsieur Vincent, whom you sent to me. For you must know that if another had come, I would in a few hours be damned, fallen into the depths of Hell. You will remember that in your village, where I had the reputation of uprightness, there was through a number of years a series of church robberies, the perpetrator of which could not be caught. But you did not know that

I was the thief, nor that year after year I went to confession and to church in order to preserve my reputation as an upright man, and out of shame never had the courage and the strength to confess what I had done. But now Monsieur Vincent has touched my heart and filled me so full of strength and of confidence in God's mercy that I acknowledge this now before you, Lady, and all who are here."

The Countess de Gondi was moved by the old man's words. She turned to Monsieur Vincent: "My God, what have I heard! Because no shepherd concerned himself about the soul of this poor man, he narrowly escaped eternal damnation, the while he lived in the people's sight as a righteous man. How desperate must be the condition of the many who do not even maintain an appearance of goodness and virtue, but are even proud of their transgressions! What can we do to save them?"

It had grown silent in the room. The peasant lay quietly on his pillow and only with his eyes did he tell his thankfulness to Monsieur Vincent, and then to the Countess, who now put a glass of water to his lips. Once more he stretched out his arms to the priest, sank back and was dead.

When the Countess returned to Folleville castle that evening she was still shaken. Restlessly she asked, again and again: "Are not we, Monsieur Vincent, are not my husband and I responsible in God's sight for the eternal salvation of the many thousands who are

our vassals? I implore you, when you preach at the
Mass tomorrow, urge them all to make good confessions of their whole lives."

Vincent promised, to put an end to the Countess's
agitation.

What had happened in the peasant home in Gannes
village was soon common knowledge, and the people
flocked to the church at Folleville to see the saintly
priest who had snatched the old man from Hell in
the hour of his death.

In his sermon Vincent de Paul spoke so vehemently,
so grippingly of the necessity of purging their souls
completely by means of a general confession that as
soon as he left the pulpit and the Mass had been said,
his confessional was besieged by penitents. The number was so large that at the hour when the people
were accustomed to return from church for the mid-
day meal, those waiting were so many that no one
could penetrate their ranks and take the priest away.

The Countess de Gondi, who beheld this with tears,
sent a messenger at once to the Jesuits at Amiens,
asking a number of the Fathers to come to Folleville.
The superior himself came and half through the night
he and another confessor assisted Monsieur Vincent.
Then the Jesuits returned to Amiens to send another
in their stead, for the number of waiting penitents did
not decrease, and this condition continued for some
days.

So gratified was the Countess that she asked Mon-

sieur Vincent to visit all parts of the Gondi domain
and urge the people everywhere to make general confessions as the best possible foundation for the rearing
of a new spiritual life.

This occurred on the 25th of January, 1617, the
Feast of the Conversion of St. Paul, and from that day
to this, the 25th of January is observed as the date
of the first of the missions to which through the
centuries a new organization of priests would devote
itself.

Countess Francoise Marguerite resolved to grant
16,000 francs for the establishment of a religious order
which would be prepared to give such beneficial
missions each five years in her domain, and she asked
Monsieur Vincent to assume the task of calling such
an order into being.

There was, however, no order, neither the Jesuits,
nor the Oratorians, to whom the Countess's gift was
offered, which was ready to undertake the work. For
the report of what had happened at Folleville spread
far and wide and many parish priests were filled, not
with joy, but with anxiety, because they feared nothing
more than being compelled to take the burden of the
cure of souls upon their shoulders and change their
own way of living.

Then, too, the nobility of the land was in possession
of many of the spiritual benefices connected with
parishes and they were apprehensive that the revenues
might be taken from them because the people now

asked for real and worthy priests in place of the holders of easy livings. Therefore the orders refrained, expecting the opposition and not daring to meet the interference which would be made in the contemplated work of soul-saving.

But the Countess, having begun this work for souls, would not allow it to die, and begged Monsieur Vincent to continue the missions in all the rural parishes within the boundaries of the Gondi lands, and to found a special community of priests to help him and to perpetuate her decision down the centuries.

A number of events intervened, however, to delay the hour when Monsieur Vincent could give himself wholly to this noble enterprise.

Chapter XI

THE SWORD OF DE ROUGEMONT

ABOUT six months later Monsieur Vincent came to Monsieur de Bérulle and begged him to listen to an especial spiritual difficulty. The founder of the Oratory was astonished and gazed at Vincent. In the face of the educator of the Gondi sons he saw fear, a hesitancy which he had seen in this countenance only once before, years ago, when Vincent bore the agony of doubt.

De Bérulle was deeply troubled.

"I doubt," began Vincent, "whether I can any longer bear the responsibility of training the three sons of the Gondi."

Monsieur de Bérulle knew the unfortunate character of young Paul de Gondi, destined to be the Archbishop of Paris, the boy who instead of a Breviary carried a Florentine dagger in his pocket.

"I have given the boy what I could, but I am only a simple man. These boys, on the contrary, are destined to fill high and powerful positions in the world. They need other teachers besides me. Yes, Heaven knows they need other teachers!"

"Is that all?" asked Monsieur de Bérulle, suspiciously. "There is another fear in your soul? What is it that frightens you?"

"There is nothing more dangerous for a poor man like me," continued Vincent, "who am the son of a peasant and began life by watching his father's sheep and pigs — nothing more dangerous than the honor and love and constant admiration which surround me in the Gondi palace and stifle me. Who am I after all? Oh, my fatherly friend, who am I that they gaze at me in amazement, as though I were a saint? That the Countess surrounds me with so much honor and attention of every sort that I cannot take a step without being enveloped by this solicitude. She no longer dares to do good, she asks only what I command her to do.

"When I leave the house in winter she sends a messenger after me to bring me a mantle, lest I feel the cold — in summer they bring me refreshments, lest I suffer thirst and heat. For if I suffered injury and died, she believes, she would be like a grape without the vine, would fall to the ground and instead of the grape ripening it would wither away on the earth. These are the suggestions of Hell! What shall I do?"

"What would you like to do?" the other asked, but as though he expected no answer.

Monsieur Vincent sprang to his feet. "I would like to go away, anywhere, to a poor parish among the peasants — to a village forsaken by its priest, where the flock has been scattered, where wolves lurk in the hills, there where I would be laughed at, mocked — there I should like to begin to save the lost."

A knock at the door. Pierre de Bérulle looked up as one of the Fathers of the Oratory entered the little room and put a letter in his hand.

De Bérulle broke the seal, read the letter and handed it to Vincent.

"It is from the superior of our Oratory in Lyons, where we established a house some weeks ago. Père Bence of Lyons begs me to find a priest for an utterly neglected parish at Chatillon, in the county of Geneva. I believe you will be glad to flee to Chatillon, for it is such a place as you described when you told me your yearning. Therefore, I as your spiritual director command you, Monsieur Vincent: Return to the palace of the Gondi, but tell no one of your intention, I bid you. Let only Monsieur du Fresne know."

Du Fresne had been the private secretary of Queen Marguerite of Valois, who had meanwhile died, and he was now living in the palace of the Gondi, where at the recommendation of Monsieur Vincent he held the post of intendant, the chief steward of the Count's estates.

Under the pretext of taking a short journey, Vincent de Paul left at once for Lyons. This was in the middle of the year 1617.

Père Bence, the Oratorians' superior in Lyons, received Monsieur Vincent and prepared him for his new task by painting for him a picture of the hardships which awaited the new parish priest of Chatillon.

For fourteen years no curé had appeared in the place. The reason was, the church had not sufficient revenues to be a desirable benefice. It had been completely neglected and now it was a mass of ruins rather than a House of God. None could be found during fourteen years who would accept the pastorate to which such a trifling income was attached. To be sure, some revenues remained, but they were in the hands of six chaplains, younger sons of aristocratic families, and these preferred to spend their incomes in worldly pleasures rather than in priestly labor. They did not even wear clerical clothes, of which they were actually ashamed. They went about attired like the noblemen of their day, pert as young beaux, with waving hair and as was customary among the officers, a mustache and a small, pointed beard. They delighted in breeding greyhounds, following the chase, having women friends and in the evening going with them to questionable inns, where worldlings gathered for gaming and feasting, to the accompaniment of performances by buffoons. And so the people of Chatillon most certainly had no worthy shepherd of their souls.

If the six chaplains lived such lives, would the people strive after the virtues which even the priests of the Lord's vineyard found too difficult to achieve and too burdensome to maintain?

When one of the chaplains came to the church occasionally to hear confessions, he did so less in order to help burdened souls than to collect fees, for the revenues being so small, insufficient to meet the expenses of these clerics' gay lives, they demanded special remuneration for every churchly function, even confessions. And the people knew that they sat in the confessionals only to get money for an evening of pleasure.

Soon nobody went to confession and a majority of the people had fallen away from the Church entirely and lived without thought of their souls' salvation, lived as they pleased. Some there were who still strove to be virtuous who had become Huguenots.

The conditions were such that Père Bence could honestly tell Monsieur Vincent he did not know how he would manage to live in the spiritual wasteland of Chatillon.

There were at Chatillon a number of families possessing immense riches, among them a Monsieur de Chassaigne, whose wife, Francoise de Mizeriac, was a friend of Madame Charlotte de Brie, the wife of Monsieur de Brunand. These families were still Catholic, it is true, but the two young wives led frivolous lives in which feast followed feast and dance followed dance, so it probably would not be prudent for a priest to ask lodging at their houses.

Also at Chatillon lived Baron Balthasar de Rougemont, nominally a Catholic, in reality a free-thinker and perhaps the worst rascal and brawler in all France. The castle of Chandee, which he owned, was near to Chatillon. But this castle of many towers and surrounded by a moat harbored guests far different from such as went forth to save souls. One drinking bout succeeded close on the other, and the drinking was interrupted only by the duels in the courtyard from time to time.

Baron de Rougemont had a sword of which he boasted to his guests because it had many times from generation to generation, saved the Rougemonts in battles and attacks by robbers. He sought day and night to prove that in all France there was no sword that could conquer the old weapon of his house. So he rode through the land, picked quarrels with strangers among the nobles and compelled them to cross swords with him. He did not even shrink from challenging old and trusting friends, so violent was his passion for personal combat, so eager was he to wield his blade and display its supremacy. At night, when the doors had been bolted, the peasants spoke in hushed voices of the deep moat around Castle Chandee, whispering that its green-glistening water hid many a gruesome secret.

So Père Bence could recommend only one house in Chatillon at which Monsieur Vincent could seek living quarters, and that was none other than the home of Monsieur de Beynier, a Huguenot. Yes, he was a Huguenot, but he was not inclined to let the gloomy creed of his fathers shadow his own life. His parents had bequeathed to him in addition to the Calvinistic faith which he esteemed little, a large fortune to the squandering of which he was now devoting his young days. He invited to his home all who pleased him, asking them to share his hospitality and his friends.

"It is a pity about this young man," said the Lyons superior. "He will not turn you away because you are a Catholic and a priest. Ask him for a room in his house. I advise you to do this and shall give you a letter to him."

With this information concerning the field of labor he was about to enter, Monsieur Vincent journeyed to Chatillon. He knocked at the door of Monsieur de Beynier, who received him hospitably and consented at once to put a room at his disposal. "Consider my house your own," said he, "and I assure you that nothing shall occur that might make your sojourn in the home of a Huguenot unpleasant. I shall tell my servants to comply with your every wish. I admit, Monsieur Vincent, that I esteem neither the faith of the Huguenots nor that of the Catholics, or even know them. I must be content to strive after the virtues of a worldling. From this time forward I hope you shall have no cause to complain of me."

There was a tinge of boastfulness in the speech of the young cavalier, a trace of satisfaction in being superior to the poor Catholic peasants, whose priest stood there homeless. De Beynier must have thought that a lot of gossip would flow through the village when it became known that a Catholic priest had to seek shelter in the house of a Huguenot.

Monsieur Vincent noticed all this, but accepted it silently and smiled. Then he asked as to the homes of

the chaplains and Monsieur de Beynier declared himself ready to supply a servant who would accompany
Monsieur Vincent wherever he wished to go.

Amazingly soon all Chatillon knew that after fourteen years a parish priest had actually come to the village, and as a result when the bell rang for Mass the
next morning its unwonted summons brought a throng
of curious people, chiefly the common folk. The
prominent and the rich held aloof.

Monsieur Vincent had the day before, the very day
of his arrival, visited the chaplains, and they were present at the Mass and all of them felt a strange embarrassment at seeing this priest come to labor here and
how his devotion and graciousness at the altar was
transmitted to the people. Old folks who had neglected
divine services for decades were moved to tears and
many of the young saw the sublime drama of the Mass
for the first time in their lives.

Even more did the new priest's words impress all
who heard him. Here, as when he undertook the pastorate at Clichy, he spoke of the sacredness of the
church, the reverence which the House of the Almighty demanded of man, as do also the human body
and soul in which the same God dwells. He called
upon his hearers to prepare their own houses, body
and soul, but also this neglected church and the whole
village of Chatillon, so that the Lord might enter in at
any hour.

"They were beautiful words," said the hardened old

people. "The new curé will be a powerful preacher. The people will listen to him a few times, but then discover that the fascinating feasts of the rich in Chatillon are after all livelier than the sermons of Monsieur Vincent."

As he had at Clichy, Monsieur Vincent on the second day began to go from house to house in Chatillon, to learn to know each villager, and he did not hesitate to enter the homes of Huguenots; and some of them, receiving him with kindly friendliness, did not fail to tell him that it must have been due to his ignorance of the circumstances that he took lodging in the house of a young man whose life was anything but exemplary, who spent his nights in feasts of indulgence with friends and women of low character. But as for Monsieur Vincent, he knew nothing to say of his host excepting that he had received him and treated him with all kindness.

The priest continued the rounds from house to house, asked after the sick and the needy, and no doubt many among those who saw him thought: How long will this zeal last? The young curé is already thirty years old. How inexperienced he is, to believe that he will have strength enough to continue even a few weeks the pace at which he has started out! If he could do that, he'd convert all Chatillon. But who could believe such a thing possible?

In those days Monsieur Vincent visited the six chaplains again and again. They were low spirited and no doubt expected him to scold them because of their manner of living. But he sat in a friendly fashion with them, stroked their greyhounds, and only once, as though incidentally, he spoke of the fact that there is no dignity on earth greater than that of the priest, for did not the Son of God give the priest something which not even the angels possess, the power to change the bread of earth into the Body and Blood of Jesus Christ and to hold the Holy Eucharist in his hands? To him, too, it was given to absolve from guilt and forgive sins. What other power on earth equaled this? Therefore, it was seemly that the priest be constantly aware of this, lest he serve the altar unworthily.

Only this did he say, then he left.

However, at the door he turned when one of the chaplains asked how they might help him. They were ready, too, they had had experience, they knew the village circumstances. The revenues of their benefices were small and it was not worth while exerting themselves on that account. Their noble families had to add to the incomes, so these younger sons of theirs in their God-forsaken benefices might live halfway according to their stations.

"Oh, I shall be glad indeed to have you help me!" exclaimed Monsieur Vincent. He let much of what they said pass by, cared only for one thing: If they would help him. He said he was about to make a list of the poor and the sick in order to provide alms for them.

The chaplains laughed: But where will Monsieur get funds for his alms?

Smiling, Vincent de Paul dug into a pocket, pulled forth a bag and divided money among the chaplains, who were to distribute it. They looked uncomfortably at each other but promised to do his bidding.

And so they went, clad as was their wont in the attire of cavaliers, with swords at their hips, through the lanes of Chatillon and inquired at the houses pointed out to them by Vincent, who had been here only a day.

This sort of thing impressed them with its novelty. One of them said it was "comical."

When they reported to the curé, as he had asked them to do, and he inquired the extent to which the needy had been supplied, they laughed again. "By Heaven, how far has the need been met? Who can have a treasure so big that the mob would not take all of it, greedily?"

Vincent de Paul had a second bag of money and he sent the chaplains out a second time. But they returned and said there still were needy ones.

Now Monsieur Vincent had no money left. Then they saw that he had given his own, too. He went to the cupboard and opened it. "I still have some linens," said he. These he had brought with him. He gave them to the chaplains, to be distributed among the sick and the poor.

At this the six clerics stood in deep embarrassment.

One put down the clothing Vincent had placed in his arms and made a defensive gesture.

"No!" And without another word he stormed out of the house, to hide what was taking place within him.

At the end of the week the village gossips told how the six chaplains had doffed their cavalier clothes and had donned attire befitting priests. Nor were they any more to be seen in the taverns, they had dismissed their riotous friends, and had even sold their cherished greyhounds.

One of the six, and he a passionate young man, the one of whom it was least expected, himself related how, roaming the fields to hunt, he met Monsieur Vincent, who greeted him genially and asked him where he was going.

"Oh, to hunt."

Then Monsieur Vincent had said: "Yes, yes, the chase is the delight of the noble. How glad I am that I was born the son of a peasant farmer and that as a boy I tended the pigs, so that it is not difficult for me to forego this sport of the nobility. For the priest is not a priest to hunt in the woods with hound and gun, and to kill animals, which are creatures of God. Our hands are consecrated for the healing of wounds inflicted by others. God give you strength to be a good priest!"

Then the curé had passed on and the chaplain's blood had rushed to his head. He had returned to Chatillon, sold his greyhound and gun that very day and given the proceeds to the poor.

Only one of the six chaplains had opposed Monsieur Vincent in the matter of demanding confession fees, said the gossips. He had told the new parish priest that he would continue to hear confessions only if the fees were paid.

Monsieur Vincent borrowed a bag of money from Monsieur de Beynier and brought it to the young chaplain, to whom he said: "O my dear friend, I see well that you still have needs and desires for the gratification of which money is necessary. So I pray you, take it from me and I will give you twice as much as you would receive if you insisted on the confession fees. But do not stain your conscience by selling absolution from sin!"

This had dumbfounded the chaplain. Recovering, he had run after Monsieur Vincent and in the open street returned the bag of money.

Before the first week had passed another strange rumor spread through the village. What queer things were happening in the house of the worldling, Monsieur Jean de Beynier? The young wastrel had told his guest that though his was the house of a Huguenot, nothing would be permitted that might offend the priest, and the self-willed host had instructed his servants to submit themselves in all things to Monsieur Vincent's orders.

On the second day of his sojourn in the house, the new curé had called the servants together and given them a daily rule, according to which they had to arise at 5 o'clock, when he would conduct morning devotions, at which they were free to be present or not, as they wished. At first the servants had come to the devotions out of idle curiosity, but then, enkindled, they had submitted wholeheartedly to the priest's rule.

Monsieur Vincent went to Lyons and returned with another priest, Monsieur Louis Girard, who was now his vicar and lived with him in Monsieur de Beynier's house and was his aide in parochial work.

The pastor and his vicar cared for their room themselves, even made their own beds, swept the floor, did all the work that ordinarily the servants would be required to do. And this they did with such winning courtesy that the servants strove to imitate their work throughout the house.

Meanwhile, Monsieur Vincent had ordered that the dissolute women who were wont to attend Monsieur de Beynier's feasts, were to be sent away and not allowed to remain in the house overnight, as that was a scandal.

Monsieur Jean de Beynier had been stunned, made speechless with consternation, had then broken into gay laughter and ordered that the priest's instructions be obeyed.

It had been observed, too, that de Beynier had, at first out of curiosity only and then with a sheerly boyish ardor assisted at the morning Mass of Monsieur Vincent and went with him to visit the poor.

In the most prominent inn of Chatillon the young blades and nobles began to complain, to talk of the madness that had seized Jean de Beynier.

During the second week of Monsieur Vincent's sojourn, the gossips of Chatillon began to tell that Monsieur de Beynier had given more than one considerable sum of money for the rebuilding of the ruined parish church, so that artisans might find employment. More than that, he had returned moneys and pieces of property to those against whom he had won a long suit in law after his father's death. He explained that he was not sure that the judge who had years before decided in his favor, had rendered a just verdict.

At the end of the second week it was noticed that Balthasar de Rougemont, the baron of Castle Chandee, had ridden to Sunday Mass. He rode up, hitched his horse in front of the church and swaggered through the people into the church.

"I must go and see," he had said. Doubtless, some of the words preached by Monsieur Vincent must have reached the bully of the castle, inducing him to see and hear for himself the man whose words, and whose deeds even more, were beginning to set the whole village afire.

After the sermon and High Mass that Sunday it was observed that the baron stood beside his horse at the church like one undecided what to do. He let the horse stand hitched, strode toward the church, halted in his tracks, like a man trying to make up his mind.

Probably he awaited Monsieur Vincent. When de Rougemont saw how the people stood gaping, he exploded with a fierce oath, swung upon his horse and galloped away.

That afternoon he came again, but this time to the house of Monsieur de Beynier and asked where Monsieur Vincent was. The priest had gone to see the poor, the servant told him. De Rougemont swore another fierce oath and rode away. But in the evening he came a third time.

Perhaps he had begun to feel uncomfortable in his castle. The servants there, questioned tirelessly by the inquisitive, said that their master seemed to have fallen into melancholia. He played with his sword, dueled with ghosts in the night. Did the graves of the murdered ones open then and the victims of his blade enter the house as nocturnal guests? Ah, now they knew why never a night came without the baron having boon companions in the castle, to carouse until morning. In this way he hoped to escape the ghostly visitors. It was not well for the Baron Balthasar de Rougemont to be alone. How many sturdy generations might be living still, striding the earth in the bloom of youth, had not de Rougemont's sword cut them down!

For some days there had not been guests at the castle. The baron had sent them away. He sat alone through the night and the murdered ones came and sat beside him. Baron de Rougemont, they seemed to say, in vain did you sink our corpses in the greenish poisonous water of the deep moat around your castle. Now our spirits rise up and summon you — to come with us.

What was it the priestling had said, he of the ruined church which he wished to rebuild? Woe to him who causes tears to flow in the eyes of widows and orphans? How many de Rougemont had made widows, how many orphans!

The rain beat on the roof of Castle Chandee. Was it the tears of all the widows and orphans of the men he had slaughtered?

And when morning came, de Rougemont staggered into the courtyard, yelled for his horse, rode wildly to the church of Chatillon. He no longer cared that the people stood gaping. He staggered into the church, threw himself heavily into the nearest pew, pillowed his restless head in his arms. He staggered to the confessional halfway through the Mass, so that children came to Monsieur Vincent and told him a man lay back there.

Fright seized the worshipers and they fled from the church when Monsieur Vincent came to hear the confession of Baron de Rougemont.

The third week since Vincent's arrival had not yet ended when there spread among the villagers the news that de Rougemont had sold the largest of his estates, that of Rougemont, the ancestral seat, had sold it at a fantastic price and given all of the money to Monsieur Vincent for distribution among the poor. The curé had commanded the baron to restrain himself, not to sell Castle Chandee too. Passers-by had heard de Rougemont say to Monsieur Girard, the vicar, who greeted him in the street. "If Monsieur Vincent permitted it, in less than a month I would cease to be the owner of the castle, no longer the lord of a bushel of grass. For is it fitting for me to live in a big castle when the Lord of Might, when He dwelt on earth, had no place whereon to lay His head?"

One day as Monsieur de Rougemont rode along he began to think of all that had happened since Monsieur Vincent's arrival, and began to examine himself as to the vices of which he had once been the abject slave. Did he regret his boon companions of the carousals? Not at all. He laughed now at the foolishness of those days.

Thus he considered one vice after the other and was filled with joy because he had overcome them, and was about to raise his hands toward Heaven to express his glad thankfulness. At that moment his mantle fell open and he saw his sword. Ah, the sword, the sword! This was the heirloom, the last, the most precious inheritance of his ancestors.

He had sold Castle Rougemont and given the proceeds to the poor. The barons de Rougemont might lose castles and forests and lands beyond the counting. One thing they would never give up, their honor. And was not this sword the last pledge and safeguard of their honor? Thus had his father once given the blade into his keeping, solemnly, as if transmitting a sacred object. He drew the sword from its scabbard. He put it to his lips, to kiss it. He let the sword, which he held with both hands at grip and tip, rest on the horse's back. He gazed forward and along the highway he saw a nobleman approaching. The hot blood of the Rougemonts stirred within him. Baron Balthasar cried out. . . . He knew what was coming — what would happen now and yet must not happen. How much blood was already clinging to his blade!

De Rougemont saw a rock by the roadside. He sprang from his horse and smashed the sword against the rock so that stone and steel lay on the ground in shattered fragments.

Then it was as if a spirit had been banished from his soul. Cheerily he mounted and rode past the nobleman as gaily as a young lover riding into Arcady.

Some years later Baron Balthasar de Rougemont died. His last possession, which he had retained at the behest of Monsieur Vincent, the Castle Chandee which he had used as a place of refuge for the poor and oppressed, this he bequeathed to the poor.

When he knew that death was near, calling the one servant he still had, he bade him go and beg the cord of a mendicant friar. And with this cord about him de Rougemont entered into the peace of God.

But before death came for the erstwhile swashbuckler who had broken his sword, the threads of other destinies were being drawn in Chatillon.

Chapter XII

MONEY CANNOT BUY A BEGGAR'S HAT

DURING Monsieur Vincent's third week in Chatillon there came to hear him preach the two noblewomen named Francoise Mizeriac and Charlotte de Brie. They came, Heaven knows, because they were inquisitive, because they had heard talk of the new priest even at their fetes and dances.

Both of the women wore costly silken gowns and adornments of fabulous value, such as had perhaps never before been seen in the village. They had asked their husbands to order the jewelry in preparation for a fete and each wished to surprise the other by wearing it on this occasion. Also, it pleased them to display themselves before the people of Chatillon who were noblemen and wealthy.

Neither of these women was really bad at heart, but both were frivolous, like butterflies flitting from one sensuous indulgence to another.

They came to hear the sermon and were so extraordinarily stirred that upon leaving the church they said to each other, "Ought we not to go back and give Monsieur Vincent a little alms for his poor? We believe he is good at heart and the misery of the poor and sick, of which he told us in his sermon, moves him deeply."

"It is said he gave his last shirt to a poor man," commented Madame Francoise. "So it would be only seemly for us to contribute a little to his work. Perhaps, too, at the fete which we are anticipating so much and for which our husbands bought us these jewels, we can do a bit of begging among the guests for this Monsieur Vincent."

"Queer sort of beggars we would make!" laughed Charlotte de Brie. "Well, let us go back."

They walked toward the priest, who had just come out of the church. They gave him a bag containing money and he accepted it with joyful thanks. Then his glance rested on the jewels.

"Pearls," said he. "Pearls are tears!"

"What do you mean, Monsieur Vincent?" asked Madame Francoise. "You mean, I suppose, that we gave you far too little for your poor, and that women who wear such costly jewels might well give more?"

"I had something different in mind," he answered.

"Will you not tell us?"

"I thought, how many tears could be wiped away with these jewels. And yet they do nothing but delight the eyes of satiated people for a few hours."

Francoise de Mizeriac blushed.

"Is there anything more we can do for you and your poor?" asked Charlotte de Brie, in embarrassment.

"Not so far as money is concerned," said Monsieur Vincent, "but if I may beg you to do so, will you not yourselves take your alms to the poor?" And he returned the bag of money to the women.

They accompanied the priest as he continued his walk and he pointed out to them the houses they were to enter. Then he left them.

That very day the news went about the village that the fete had been cancelled which had been scheduled for the residence of the Mizeriacs and for which the aristocrats and the rich had already prepared. Madame de Mizeriac had returned intensely moved and completely changed from her visits to the homes of the poor.

In the days that followed one saw the two self-willed young women walking demurely in the streets of Chatillon, garbed in modest clothes, shy and fearful lest anybody see them enter and then later leave one of the village's miserable homes.

On a Sunday toward the end of August, the two noblewomen came to Monsieur Vincent before his sermon and implored him to tell, when he preached, of the abandoned tenant family in a lonely home out beyond the village. They were sick, the father and mother and all of the children, so they could not care for themselves. And they lacked even food and drink and medicine. The women would gladly do all they could, but they knew it was his desire, they told the priest, that a constantly increasing number of people in his parish be aroused to the doing of good deeds. However, if his appeal found no response, very well, they would themselves care for the family. So Monsieur Vincent told his listeners of the poor people in the lonely house.

After the Mass, the priest and the noblewomen set out to visit the tenant family. But on the way thence they saw, stretching along the meadow, a pilgrim stream of people carrying all sorts of goods in baskets, and when Monsieur Vincent reached the house almost all of Chatillon was gathered there, and what they had brought was so much that the priest smiled with joy at such a manifestation of love and gestured with his hands and cried out: "Ah, the foolishness of love! Only a small proportion of all this is required for the present needs of the poor and sick in this house. But you have brought so much that a large part of your sacrifices will be spoiled before it can be used, and then in a short time the need will be present again."

And he began to collect the offerings, that they might be prudently stored and divided according to a definite plan.

The next day he called Francoise de Mizeriac and Charlotte de Brie, and bade them find out whether there were not in Chatillon a number of women, not too many, he said, about fifteen at the beginning, who would join them in establishing a Conference of Charity.

In his hand Monsieur Vincent held a little piece

of paper on which he had written a rule for the organization, providing for the collection of alms and supplies and for their systematic distribution. The women of the conference would be given a steward, who would manage the treasury and do all other things for which men are better fitted. And Vincent de Paul bade his host, Monsieur de Beynier, accept this office. De Beynier had renounced the creed of the Huguenots and returned to the ancient faith, and he was henceforth one of the most generous men in Chatillon.

So the ladies met and took counsel of each other and what Monsieur Vincent had prescribed in the rule, that they did. He had thought of even the smallest details — a week's schedule, how much white bread each sick person was to receive, how much meat, and not forgetting a quantity of wine, nor what they were to receive whose sickness demanded special food.

He regulated the activity of the women, whom he called the Servants of Charity, in such a way that all the poor and sick who were accepted for help by the conference were carefully listed, lest any be forgotten or neglected. The Servants of Charity were instructed to devote themselves alternately according to a stated arrangement, to the care of the sick and poor, and this service of love they were to perform themselves, not delegate it to their servants. They were also to take care that when food was brought to the sick, it be taken first to those who had others in their homes to help them, and then to those who were alone, so that in the latter cases the ladies could remain with the sick and bring cheer into their loneliness.

The repast was to be carefully prepared, with a white linen cloth on the table or bed, so the meal would take on something of a festive character. The rule provided, too, that the visitors were to bring flowers with them when they called on the sick or poor. These alms, Monsieur Vincent said, were the least expensive of all, for the meadows offered an unlimited supply of them free of cost.

Then the women were to cut the meat as the sick person might require and offer it with words of Christian charity. They ought to sit beside the ones they are visiting and converse, dwelling on the intimate affairs of daily life, and reminding them of what had been beautiful and of sweet memory in the past and also of what they might still possess, so the hearts of them would know a measure of happiness. And they were to direct the minds and hearts of the sick to the richest of treasures, the highest good God gives His children — love.

After he had tested the Servants of Charity carefully for some three months, Monsieur Vincent caused the rule of the conference to be examined and approved by the Archbishop of Lyons, and on the 8th of December in the year 1617 he celebrated the dedication of the first conference in the restored church of Chatillon.

Shortly thereafter, before the year had come to an

end, Vincent de Paul was compelled to leave Chatillon, to which his labors had brought so many blessings. But the conference, before another year had passed, was to rescue the whole village from the direst need. The year 1618 brought a prolonged drought and with it, famine. Then it was that Monsieur de Beynier, steward of the Servants of Charity, supplied the poor and those who had no work from a warehouse which he had filled with grain. This he accomplished by means of his own generous offerings and the contributions which the conference members collected throughout the town.

Then the plague followed the famine. All of the rich fled in haste from their country homes and estates at Chatillon, to escape the contagion. But Francoise de Mizeriac and Charlotte de Brie did not flee. Near the outskirts of the village they erected a wooden shelter and there they lived and from thence went forth to carry on in the midst of the plague the work of charity begun by Monsieur Vincent. At the risk of their lives they brought the offerings of this charity and the medicines to the huts of those stricken with the dread disease; and in those days of supreme need and misery Chatillon's people who were near to despair found their last and single hope in the goodness and pity of the Servants of Charity, who brought them both the only earthly help there was and the solace of Heaven.

And all this had come to pass because of the brief

sojourn, scarcely six months, of Monsieur Vincent in the village of Chatillon.

When Vincent came to the town in the summer of 1617, the worries that had driven him from the palace of the Gondi had loomed so gigantically in his soul that he saw nothing else. Therefore it escaped him that he had abandoned a field the tilling of which he had started but by no means completed.

Soon after his arrival in Chatillon Monsieur Vincent had written to the Count de Gondi, Commander of the Galleys of the King, telling him what had happened, stating frankly that he did not consider himself qualified to carry forward the education of the Count's sons, and begging de Gondi to release him from his service.

The Count de Gondi was deeply affected by Monsieur Vincent's letter. No one in his house, least of all his wife the Countess, had had the slightest intimation that Vincent, who seemed so indispensable in the place, had not merely gone on a short journey, that he would not return to the palace.

The Count wrote to his wife, telling her his trouble and disappointment and bidding her neglect nothing she might deem advisable to do to induce Monsieur Vincent to change his decision.

The Countess received the news on the Feast of the Exaltation of the Cross, and when she had read her husband's letter she cried out complainingly: "For me a cross has in truth been set up this day!"

So incomprehensible did it seem to her that Monsieur Vincent should have left her house, that she neither ate nor found sleep at night. She wept continuously and overwhelmed her servants with questioning as to what might possibly have been neglected, what might induce him to return.

"O God," she cried, "are we, my husband, my children and I and the vassals entrusted to us, less worthy of being saved than the people of Chatillon?"

She considered it impossible, after the priest's departure, to save her own soul and continue and complete the work she had so courageously begun under the direction of her spiritual adviser. In truth, she clung even more tenaciously than Vincent himself to the plan of covering the whole land with missions and to rescue it thereby from spiritual ruin. The idea had originated with her. However, though first to conceive the task, she was not strong enough to carry it into execution. Therefore, now that Monsieur Vincent was lost to her and to the plan, she held all to be lost. Weeping, she came to Monsieur Pierre de Bérulle, imploring him to send Monsieur Vincent back to the house of the Gondi. She also went to see the Archbishop of Paris. She appealed to all of whom she believed that they cherished Vincent and might influence him to come back. Then she wrote to Monsieur Vincent, sending with her letter the one she had received from her husband and a note of Monsieur de Bérulle's in which he gave Vincent de

Paul permission to leave his parish. All this she dispatched to Chatillon with great care by a messenger.

The messenger returned to say Monsieur Vincent bade him inform the Countess that, having considered the matter carefully, he was convinced that it was God's will for him to remain in Chatillon.

In spite of this refusal, the Countess de Gondi did not relax her efforts to bring back the spiritual director for herself and her house and her vassals.

She went to the monasteries, she besought the religious orders to storm Heaven with petitions she induced all to write to Monsieur Vincent, so no week passed without letters from Paris imploring him to come back.

But she herself did not write — she caused the Fathers of the oratory to write, one after the other — her children wrote, even the reckless Jean Paul wrote, he who had rather carry in his pocket a Florentine dagger than the Breviary.

Finally she sent Monsieur du Fresne to Chatillon with a bundle of letters from her sons, her servants, the Archbishop of Paris, Monsieur de Bérulle.

Monsieur Vincent received his old friend with joy, but consternation seized him when he read the letters and became aware of the anxiety of all the writers as to the spiritual and general welfare of the Countess de Gondi. And now for the first time he too began to realize that in truth the first mission at Folleville had been the cornerstone of an edifice, the building of which was now endangered.

This affected him so much that he became the victim of tormenting uncertainties and journeyed to Lyons to consult Père Bence, superior of the Oratorians there. He let himself be advised by his friends in Lyons and by Monsieur du Fresne to have his vicar, Monsieur Louis Girard, remain as administrator of his parish.

His people learned of his departure only when he preached his farewell sermon. Amazement came into the faces of the hundreds who on a Sunday in December heard him bid them this wholly unexpected adieu.

"When I came among you, I believed I would remain here until the end of my days. But it is God's will that I leave you now," he said.

Then some in the church began to weep loudly and soon the whole congregation was a chorus of lamentation.

Immediately after the sermon and Mass, Monsieur Vincent left Chatillon. He had prepared in secret for this journey, had bequeathed his scanty belongings to the poor and to the beggars. Even his hat he had given away, so he set forth like one plundered by robbers, but with the whole village for escort. His people wished to show him their love and esteem on this last opportunity. Many ran for hours alongside the carriage that took him away.

To the beggar to whom Monsieur Vincent had given

his old hat, came rich people offering to buy it, offering large sums of money. But the beggar scorned all, even the most generous inducements. He would rather run the risk of hunger, actually suffer hunger, than part with the hat.

Chapter XIII

HIS BROTHERS: THE GALLEY SLAVES

VINCENT DE PAUL returned to Paris on the 23rd of December, 1617. He called on his friend, Monsieur de Bérulle, who now released him from obedience, offered him complete freedom of activity. The Oratorian felt that he was not qualified any longer to direct one whom he held to be far greater than himself.

Thus Monsieur Vincent returned to the Gondi palace at Christmas and was received with jubilation, such as the coming of an angel would arouse. His difficulties as to the further education of the sons of the Count and Countess were removed by the appointment of other tutors, who, however, remained subordinate to him.

The priest's burning desire to help above all the souls of the country folk, was seconded by the Count and Countess with all possible generosity and energy. Monsieur Vincent drew up a comprehensive plan which provided for missions in every village of all the de Gondi lands. As soon as spring came to France, Vincent rode out into the country, often accompanied by Emmanuel de Gondi and the Countess, and in many parts of their domains the mission of Folleville was repeated. But now the priest combined with each mission the organization of a Conference of Charity for women, and also a conference for men. Soon this work of love was spread throughout the de Gondi estates and beyond them to other parts of the land. There spread throughout France something of such proportions, of such implications that not until later epochs was its extent entirely revealed, wholly appreciated.

Having returned with the Count de Gondi to Paris from one of these mission journeys and looking about for new fields of action, Monsieur Vincent beheld in spirit the dismal prisons of the Conciergerie.

He knew that in these prisons languished many condemned men who would be sent to Marseilles or Bordeaux to begin their long sentences as galley slaves. He recalled, too, that all of these prisoners were subject to his master, Count Philippe-Emmanuel de Gondi, Commander of the King's Galleys.

Thereupon the priest sought and obtained from the Commander permission to visit the Conciergerie. When the gate of the first prison was opened to him he remembered keenly, no doubt, the hardships and anguish which had been his as a slave in Tunis. But he shrank at the gloom and dampness of the passageways that led below the earth's surface, as if they were anterooms of Hell.

Were these prisons? Weren't they but holes hewn out of the rock, with water dripping down? And there

languished the miserable wretches. With chains welded
to their bodies they lay huddled in a mass of ragged,
dirty, vermined humanity.

From the darkness the faces of the condemned men
loomed spectral and unhealthy, and a filth of words
poured out of their mouths when they saw it was
a priest who was being led toward them. A curse was
shouted, hellish laughter echoed against the moldy
walls of rock.

"O my brothers, how you have sunk to the level
of animals!" Monsieur Vincent cried out and looked
at the men with horror. But also with pity. Stretched
his hands out to them. They kicked at him. His own
hands were cold and moist and to them clung the
filth they had encountered.

Vincent de Paul staggered upward into the sun-
light. Where had he been? The curses reverberated
in his ears. Thunderingly the gate was shut behind
him. He stood in the open and looked about. If the
sinister walls were not there in all their dismal bulk,
he would have believed that what he had seen was
an evil dream.

Moved to the depths of his soul, he hurried back
to the city, to the commander of all the royal galleys
of France, and told him the horrors he had seen.

"Are not they, too, children of the Almighty Father?
Granting that they have been plunged into this misery
because they committed crimes, for which they will
be sternly punished through many years, perhaps until

the end of their lives — does not the responsibility for the future rest on us? Who has a right to call them the scum of humanity? Who will wipe the scabs of Hell from their faces, so that what is beneath may become visible — the souls which God breathed into them?"

Monsieur Vincent begged de Gondi for God's sake to take the prisoners from the Conciergerie.

"It is not within your power to break their chains, but it is within your power to take away all that must be taken away so these condemned men may realize their destiny and find their way home to their Creator in spite of all their misery and all their sins."

De Gondi, stirred tremendously by Vincent's report, yielded at once to the impassioned pleading and permitted and commissioned the priest to find a house that would serve the purpose of a prison without violating the human dignity of the men confined there.

Vincent de Paul hurried out into the streets and alleys of Paris that very evening, and near the Church of Saint-Roche he found a house, and rented it; rented it without knowing whether he would have the money with which to pay for it. He would beg in the streets, if necessary, he would go to the houses of the rich.

Hurrying again to the Conciergerie cells with the Commander's delegated power, he ordered the men under sentence to the galleys to be brought up from their dark and dank caverns to the light of day. This was done, and when they sat in the courtyard he walked among the prisoners. They gazed at him. They breathed deeply in the open air.

Why had they been brought up here?

Men sentenced to the galleys were confined in the prisons of Paris until the number of them was large enough to form what was called a "chain." When a "chain" could be formed, the tragic journey continued to Marseilles, where the King's fleet lay at anchor.

At this time the number of prisoners in Paris was not large, for a consignment had left a few weeks before, bound for the port and the galley ships.

What did he wish, this quixotic priest who sat down beside them, touched their wounds where the chains on arms and ankles had caused large, painful sores?

Many a one among these men still had in his eyes the despair that had taken possession of him when he heard the judge's sentence, "To the galleys!" Many a one was not yet reconciled to his fate, was rebellious still. Others were stubborn and had become hardened, but even they realized that this priest, whatever else he desired, had revolted against the infernal holes in which they had been chained and had fought to give them a few hours up here in the sunny courtyard. God only knew how he had managed it, through whom.

Now he spoke to them of their condition. "O brothers for Jesus Christ's sake!"

Brothers for the sake of Jesus Christ? . . . Brothers, he had said! . . . So that the hellish laughter would not sound again. . . . Brothers for the sake of Christ!

He bent down to one, drew a piece of linen from his coat pocket, bandaged a wound. The prisoner submitted grumblingly, gazed suspiciously at the priest.

". . . One thing you mustn't do, talk to me of the good God!"

No, of Him Monsieur Vincent would not speak, as long as the prisoners were in such a pitiless condition.

"I cannot help you evade the fate which your crimes have brought upon you. But you, my brothers for the sake of Jesus Christ, must not therefore despair. Help me, I beg you, help me to rescue you from the misery into which you would allow yourselves to sink." This he said to all of them.

He spoke of their relatives, he wrote down their addresses so he could let them know how the prisoners fared. He distributed gifts.

Thereupon the maledictions ceased.

And when the guards came to take the men back underground, Monsieur Vincent stood at the opening and held out his arms to them and spoke to each one: "Do not despair, my brother. I shall come again. . . . I shall come tomorrow, I shall not miss a single day."

And he came the next day, and the next, as he had promised.

Who was this kindly fool? He must have gained permission and have the power to make even the guards obey him.

Then came the day on which the big gates of this

prison opened upon the meadow and through the meadow Monsieur Vincent led the condemned men who followed him in their chains, led them to their new place of confinement.

No day passed on which he did not visit the men he had led to the new prison, and no day on which he did not go to those left behind in the rocky holes of dark misery.

And it came to pass that down to the deepest of the underground cells he brought his chalice, and kneeling among the condemned men, offered up a Mass. At this the first man of them all began to weep. Vincent spoke of the Giver of all good gifts, who would never forsake them, who was with them even in this place.

Then the scales of Hell fell from the faces of these men.

In their prison, Monsieur Vincent held a mission for the criminals, a mission such as he had given for the peasants at Folleville.

In Paris, in the streets and in the homes of the rich, even at the royal court, the story of what was happening was on all lips. Many who heard that the priest had said it was God's will to visit the prisons, thronged to the place, burghers and inquisitive lords and ladies, and in the courtyards beheld the miracle that had been worked, and filled the pockets of Monsieur Vincent with alms money.

Then the news reached the ears of the King. He

bade his Commander of the Galleys, the Count de
Gondi, submit a report; and then he summoned
Monsieur Vincent into his presence and appointed
him Chief Pastor of the Galley Slaves and gave him
the rank of an officer and empowered him to enter all
prisons and to board all the royal galleys.

When these things had been done, Vincent journeyed to Marseilles.

In Paris, Monsieur Vincent had seen only the men
on the threshold of the fate which is that of the galley
slaves. In the prisons of Marseilles he found those
who had for years suffered in body and soul all that
the galley oarsmen must endure.

And there was repeated at Marseilles what had
taken place at Paris.

Monsieur Vincent besieged the General of the
Galleys with pleas for a hospital, to care for the
slaves who became ill on the ships or who had grown
old or were wholly broken under the relentless rigor
of their toil.

Then he himself boarded the galleys and went
out to sea.

One day Monsieur Vincent came to the port of
Marseilles to find out whether an expected galley had
put in. The men on this vessel were to be relieved
of their strenuous work for a time, while another
galley, now ready to sail, took its place in the
royal fleet.

He came upon an old woman, weeping disconsolately. He asked her why she wept, sought to console her.

The old woman told him, amid her tears, that her son, falsely accused, had been sentenced and was now on the galley which was ready to put out to sea. This son had been her only support. He left behind him a sick wife and small children in a poor little hut. But what was such misery compared to his, innocently condemned to the galleys, exposed to a horrible fate?

Vincent de Paul knew full well that he could not reverse the judge's sentence, for it happened often that as only the worst of crimes were punished with condemnation to the galleys and the galley slaves died in huge numbers, the prisons would not contain enough new men to supply the ships. And then more than one unjust sentence was pronounced. What was he to do?

He bade the weeping woman wait for him on the pier. He boarded the waiting galley and soon found the young prisoner, seated in deep despair at his oar. The officers were not yet in their places, the guards complied with the priest's request, he showing them the royal commission. He knelt beside the despairing young man and took off his chains. He told him not to ask any questions and then exchanged clothes with him. The guards would have dashed forward to prevent this, but Vincent made use of his prerogative as an officer of the King, commanded the overseers to obey and put him in the chains that had bound the old woman's son. Vincent was there to take his place.

Utterly amazed, unable to grasp this impossible thing that had happened, the liberated slave hurried away.

One hour later the galley put out to sea.

When Monsieur Vincent failed to return to the Gondi palace that night and this was reported to Count Emmanuel, he was troubled; but as the priest was wont to frequent the most miserable quarters of the city to do deeds of kindness, it was taken for granted that he was too much engrossed in his work of mercy to come back to the palace and had stayed elsewhere overnight.

However, as the days passed and the priest did not appear, an anxious unrest seized General de Gondi and he sent out many messengers, but none could find Monsieur Vincent.

Now the Chief Pastor of the Galleys had brought it about that two priests were to board each galley as soon as it put to shore. One of these priests discovered Vincent de Paul among the slaves. At once this was made known to de Gondi, who himself went to the ship and released his friend.

For weeks the one-time slave in Tunis had lived the life of the galley oarsmen, had borne on his body the welts of blows delivered by the heartless overseers who did not know that it was he who sat on the bench, swung the oar.

Monsieur Vincent was scarcely able to walk. His

legs were swollen and discolored. The wounds which
the chains had inflicted on his feet remained a source
of pain to him for the remainder of his life, more
than forty years.

From Marseilles Vincent went to Bordeaux, where
ten galleys lay at anchor, and there repeated his Good
Samaritan's solicitude among the slaves.

Then he gathered priests about him and collected
money and sent his associates to Tunis and Algeria,
to console the Christian slaves in their pitiless captivity, to save them from the final despairing plunge into
Hell, and to ransom as many of them as possible.

Disguised, Vincent de Paul's associates penetrated
into the prisons, let themselves be locked up with
the condemned men, and brought them the Holy
Eucharist.

Clad as physicians, these dauntless priests dared even
to invade the houses of Musselmans, under the pretext
of curing the sick slaves. The Mohammedan masters
permitted this, as they did not wish to incur the loss
which the death of a slave entailed. Thus the co-
workers of Monsieur Vincent were able to bring the
poor captives the supreme medicine, the Bread of
Angels.

But one of the disguised priests, being discovered,
suffered death by fire.

Later another, together with twenty-two fellow
Christians, was bound to the mouth of a Musselman's
cannon and in that manner suffered martyrdom.

Of the twenty-five thousand Christian slaves in Algiers, Monsieur Vincent had, before he died, liberated twelve thousand. To all the others he had brought the solace which made it possible for them to bear even so cruel a fate as theirs.

Chapter XIV

Amazement at Mâcon

ON ONE of his journeys through France — this was in the year 1621 — Monsieur Vincent came to the city of Mâcon. He intended to remain only one day and one night, then resume his trip to Paris. But he found Mâcon flooded with beggars who halted all passers-by, halted them insistently, even saucily, and almost plundered them, instead of asking for alms, as beseems beggars.

When Monsieur Vincent saw this and noticed that among the beggars were able-bodied men who might well earn their bread by working, he spoke to a number of them, asked how it came that they idled in the streets to get trifling alms while not far beyond the city the peasants lacked enough hands for the harvesting of their crops. The answers he received made it clear to him that here was a neglected group, shying away from labor, preferring to live on what could be extracted from the well-to-do citizens and pass their days in idle laziness. They knew nothing of Christian teaching and nobody admonished them. The priests did not bother themselves about these beggars, but the people who were expected to give and give, considered them a plague in the city, like a swarm of locusts descended upon a field of grain.

Monsieur Vincent went to the Bishop of Mâcon and told him what he had seen. But the Bishop told Vincent that no man knew how to cure the plague.

A number of canons who were present, hearing Vincent begin to tell the Bishop that the lives of the beggars demanded a reformation, began to laugh loudly and to say that they, too, were priests and understood what to do with people, but as to these beggars there was nothing to be done. Mendicants could very well be managed when they numbered few in a town. A number of circumstances had impoverished a large number of people in Mâcon in former years and these had never managed to rise from the depths of poverty to regain a position of property ownership and comfort. Thus the city had come to the edge of serious trouble. No one knew what to do.

The Bishop of Mâcon, however, said that if Monsieur Vincent believed he could alter the situation, he was to proceed with all possible means. Perhaps it would be well for the priest to consult the city councilmen, to learn from them whether the situation was really hopeless.

Monsieur Vincent departed, visited the councilors, listened to their complaints, their laughter, and their scorn — but he also inquired as to citizens who might be willing to help him in his work of rescue. Thus it happened that Vincent de Paul remained in Mâcon.

Before a week had passed, Vincent had organized Conferences of Charity for women and for men, and had succeeded in inducing the city officials to proclaim that all beggars, whether honestly in need or because they would not work, must be registered. Any who refused to be thus listed would receive no alms in Mâcon.

Further than this, at Vincent's bidding the councilors forbade the citizens to give any alms excepting through the Conferences of Charity.

At first, the throng of beggars was filled with consternation. What did it mean? Why must they be registered? Were they to be cast into prison? And a number of them fled the city. Others, because they were suspicious of the list, hurried to find employment and from that basis of security watched the turn of events. Perhaps the hour would come when this queer Monsieur Vincent would leave Mâcon as suddenly as he had entered the city.

Even those actually poor and sick were afraid to let their names be registered, but finally their need compelled them to do so. And then they learned that on specified days of the week they would receive alms and each time a supply sufficient to keep them at least from the extremity of want for a week's time.

Now Monsieur Vincent divided the poor into two groups, those who were weak or crippled in body and therefore unable to work, and those who were too lazy to work and for that reason resorted to begging. The latter received alms, it is true, but at the same time were assigned to labor which they had to perform in return for the help given them.

The city fathers of Mâcon, at Monsieur Vincent's bidding, established a public employment bureau, as a result of which an additional number of the beggars disappeared.

Beggars who were sick and had no kith nor kin to care for them were gathered into a municipal hospital. The others were cared for by the men and women of the Conferences of Charity, in their homes and in the way Monsieur Vincent had prescribed in other cities.

Then Monsieur Vincent sent his Servants of Charity to seek out the poor who were in actual need but received few alms or none at all because they hesitated to make their condition known and because the bold and unworthy mendicants had monopolized the gifts of love.

In three weeks all this had been accomplished. A wonderment, a veritable amazement took hold of the whole city. A stranger had come, had seen the need, had met and supplied it and gone his way again.

The city fathers met to arrange for a feast at which to thank Monsieur Vincent publicly. But he, having learned what threatened him, departed at once and was not to be found when they came to escort him to the feast.

Third Book: Good Deeds Without End

A mantle of mercy for foundlings.

Chapter XV

FOR THE COUNTRY FOLK

WHEN Monsieur Vincent returned from Chatillon to the palace of the Gondi at Christmas, 1617, the Countess implored the spiritual director whom she had won back to promise never to leave the house again.

Since that first mission at Folleville the Countess Francoise had sought constantly to find a religious order which would accept her founding donation of 16,000 livres, with the agreement to conduct such missions each five years in all parishes throughout the Gondi estates. She believed she would miss the goal of her life if she failed to accomplish this for the salvation of her vassals' souls. And now there was no one who could help her excepting only Vincent de Paul.

She had taken counsel of her husband and together they had gone to the Archbishop of Paris, the Count's brother, and the three had agreed that Monsieur Vincent must be induced to found a new society whose members would bind themselves to give missions in rural parishes.

Then they consulted Vincent de Paul and after the whole matter had been thoroughly considered, he gave his consent.

On the 17th of April in the year 1625, the plans had advanced to such an extent that the founding charter of the Congregation of the Missions could be signed by the Count and Countess de Gondi, whose donation now amounted to 45,000 livres. In addition, Monsieur Vincent was presented with the Ecole des Bonne Enfants, an ancient foundation now lying abandoned in Paris. Into this he could gather the priests who joined his society.

On the day the charter was signed, Vincent de Paul made a renunciation of all the offices and benefices and dignities which had until then been given him.

He and the priests who joined him obligated themselves to lead a common life in the house which had been given to Vincent. Only he was exempted, because he would continue to reside in the Gondi palace. (This rule remained in effect until the Countess de Gondi died; thereafter Vincent was completely free to devote himself entirely to the Congregation of the Missions.)

The new missionaries were forbidden to preach in the cities, so that they would not deviate from the chief purpose of the organization, the care of souls in the country. Neither was their association to be a new order in the sense of the old monastic institutions. For they were to live among the people and not withdrawn like the monks. Therein lay the new element, hitherto unknown.

When these matters became known in Paris, the

clerical circles became seriously alarmed and united in sending delegations to the King and to Parliament in efforts to prevent an official confirmation of the new congregation. They feared lest the excessive zeal of Vincent de Paul and his missionaries disturb them in the comfortable ease they had hitherto enjoyed. They spoke, too, of intruders who would come into parishes where they had no business to be. One sent missionaries to the heathens, said these clerics, not to people who were by baptism already won for Christ's kingdom and whom one ought as a consequence to let in peace.

But the objections of the Parisian ecclesiastics found no support in Parliament.

In 1626 the Congregation of the Missions was approved by the Archbishop of Paris; a year later by the King of France, and again six years later (in 1633) by the Pope, in spite of the opposition which had reached even as far as Rome.

At first there were only a few priests whom Monsieur Vincent selected for his great project. These soon began to leave the College of the Good Children in Paris to conduct their missions in the country. They would place the key of the house with a neighbor during their absences.

Soon the evident blessing which rested on the work caused a constantly increasing number of priests to apply for admission. The house was filled with missionaries and Monsieur Vincent was at his wits' end to find ways of mastering the growth of his congregation. Then, when his need was greatest, there came to him the Prior of the monastery of Saint-Lazare, that stood in massive dignity along the road from Paris to Saint-Denis. The prior had become involved in difficulties with his monks. Originally a hospital for lepers, Saint-Lazare had in the course of time become a great religious feudal domain, with estates scattered through the land and juridical authority of its own over all the vassals dwelling on its estates. This authority was exercised by the Prior, who was appointed by the Archbishop of Paris and confirmed in his office by the King.

The monastery's riches had led the monks to live carelessly and despite the huge revenues from its wide domains, it had gradually fallen into decay. There were scarcely any lepers left in the building. The foundation had survived its original purpose. Now the vast building stood useless and the Prior could not get along well with the monks. So he wished to relinquish his office and looked about for one into whose hands he might place it. He bethought himself of Monsieur Vincent and his young Congregation of the Missions, went to see Vincent and offered him the priory and its property.

When Vincent de Paul heard what was offered him, he was dumbfounded. He had scarcely finished a prayer for help and here was this prelate offering him an immense foundation with extensive possessions and generous revenues.

"Your hands are trembling, Monsieur Vincent," observed the Prior.

"I must confess that your offer has bewildered me," answered Vincent. "Give me a little time in which to consider it."

"What? You wish time to consider it? You are in desperate need, I offer you help, and you wish to consider it?"

"We are poor priests. What shall we do with such riches?"

And it seemed to him that this tender of building and lands might be a temptation of Hell. No, no, he would not accept it!

"Consider well," said the Prior. "In half a year I shall return."

He came again, believing that Vincent's need would have increased to such an extent that now the queer priest would gladly accept the offer.

The need had increased, it is true. But Vincent de Paul was still convinced that the offer was a temptation. He thanked the Prior for his generous proposal, but declined a second time to accept it.

All who heard of the matter were filled with astonishment and the head of Saint-Lazare had recourse to the Archbishop of Paris, and hurried to see all who knew Vincent and all whom he believed influential with him. The leader of the Congregation of the Missions was to be compelled to take the priory.

Week succeeded week, month followed month.

Finally Monsieur Vincent consented to submit the case to an impartial referee and to abide by the arbitrator's decision. The arbitrator declared that it was Vincent's duty to accept the priory and Vincent bowed to the verdict.

However, when this became known, some ecclesiastics and the monks of Saint-Lazare joined in instituting a suit in court to prevent the transfer of the property to the Congregation of the Missions, which they thoroughly disliked. Only because he was forced to do so did Monsieur Vincent enter into the court controversy, and he prayed many times, not that the decision should favor him, but that the verdict might indicate God's will in the matter.

The secular court confirmed the transfer of Saint-Lazare to the mission priests and Vincent de Paul and his colleagues moved into the building, but lived apart from the monks there.

Saint-Lazare had been neglected, soon it became apparent that even its extensive revenues would not suffice to pay for the necessary repairs. Vincent fought against the further deterioration of the building and battled for the maintenance of the foundation and its revenues, so that he could use them for the poor.

Thus Saint-Lazare became the headquarters of Monsieur Vincent's mission priests, who soon became known as Lazarists, because of the name of their house.

Later, Monsieur Vincent gave earnest thought to the healing of one of the most serious wounds of the

Church in his days, the spiritual condition of the priests. Since his congregation was not allowed to give missions in Paris, he decided, upon the advice of a Bishop, to arrange for retreats at Saint-Lazare. That Bishop and Vincent de Paul conceived the idea that young men studying for the holy priesthood, before they received the first Holy Orders ought to be gathered together for a few weeks and instructed in all they ought to know in order to fulfill their priestly work conscientiously.

There were at the time many priests, pastors of parishes, who did not even know the words of absolution or Consecration; many did not know the whole of the Our Father. In Paris, a pilgrim who went from church to church might see how the Holy Sacrifice of the Mass was celebrated differently in each one; for the priests, not knowing the Mass, did each as he deemed best. Some walked about the altar and said *Dominus vobiscum* a few times, and Monsieur Vincent, who was present on such an occasion, cried out that it was pitiful to see those poor priests in their complete helplessness. But how could it have been otherwise, when so many bishoprics in France were in such a sad state that one was held by a married musician and another by a breeder of dogs who had for seventeen years never seen the inside of a church.

So thorough had been the penetration of secular power in the Church and so grievously had the kingdom of Christ been devastated that holy men arose in

those days, stirred by God, to imitate Christ in cleansing the temple of Jerusalem.

Monsieur Vincent, one of the awakened, began now
to offer spiritual exercises at Saint-Lazare for pastors
and other priests already in the sacerdotal office. Designated priests came to the place each Tuesday and
joined what was called the Tuesday Association.

Such retreats in common and such meetings with
the purpose of cleansing the soul and advancing in
perfection and finally achieving salvation, had not been
heard of hitherto. Soon cardinals and bishops, but also
holders of worldly dignities, nobles of high rank, officers of the law courts, even officers of the army and
soldiers flocked to Saint-Lazare for the spiritual
exercises.

Monsieur Vincent welcomed them all as his guests,
though often enough he did not know how he would
find room, provide food for all of them.

Once an associate came to him and said, "Monsieur
Vincent, among our guests are some who have come
again and again, not because they are honestly desir-
ous of taking the Bread of Angels and God's holy
words of doctrine, but because they can rest com-
fortably here for a few days and let themselves be fed."

Vincent smiled and answered, "Ought I to turn
them away for that reason? Which of us knows whether
those who take advantage of us now, as they must out
of courtesy be present at the instructions, will not hear
and keep a word that will some time in their lives,

perhaps not until they are at death's door, help them to save their souls?"

From year to year the Congregation of the Missions grew and it began to establish branches of its work throughout the land. An entirely new training for those who wished to become priests, the seminary courses, evolved from this early venture of Vincent de Paul.

Nobody knew at the time that from the humble beginnings in which Monsieur Vincent cradled his mission organization, Divine Providence would recruit the first company of those Soldiers of Charity who would soon enter upon a fierce struggle against the raging forces of Hell.

Chapter XVI

THE STORY OF MADEMOISELLE LE GRAS

WHEREVER they held missions, the priests associated with Monsieur Vincent founded the first societies of Christian charity, the Conferences of Charity, men's and women's.

In Paris, too, a conference had been organized. Composed chiefly of women of the nobility, many of the members followed gladly in the footsteps of the two noblewomen of Chatillon who had given themselves entirely to the care of the poor. But in Paris, in proximity to the royal court, many of these ladies encountered the adverse comments and various hindrances placed in their path by their husbands because the women wished to be attired in the modest clothes of a maidservant when they visited the needy. Nor was it seemly that these aristocratic ladies should prepare soups with hands on which jewels sparkled, and carry the broth to the sick. Therefore, partly out of shyness, partly because they would not persevere, these women of noble families instead of performing the works of mercy themselves, sent their servants to the poor. But the servants grumbled, did not wish to do such work. The result was that the service of the poor in and about Paris encountered grave difficulties.

When the serious damage became evident — it was in the year 1624 — Monsieur Vincent betook himself to a young widow of noble family, Mademoiselle Le Gras. (At that time in France the wives and also the widows of the lower nobles were addressed as Mademoiselle.)

Louise de Marillac was the widow of Monsieur Le Gras and was born in 1591, ten years later than Vincent de Paul. Already at thirteen years of age she became an orphan. Her uncle, who held the rank of duke, wished to take care of her, but she voiced a desire to join the Capuchin nuns. She was of delicate health and the convent refused to admit her.

At the age of 22, Louise de Marillac was married by her uncle to Monsieur Le Gras and to the son she bore him she devoted herself with generous love. Throughout her life he was the cause of many worries to her.

Mademoiselle Le Gras kept her eyes fixed on eternal things, which she had yearned for since childhood, and so she visited the sick and the poor as much as possible, to console them in Christian charity and help them as far as was within her power.

In 1623 Monsieur Le Gras became critically ill and as she nursed him Louise suffered an extraordinary spiritual fear. She feared that this sickness had come upon her husband and that he would be taken from her because she had not been more persistent in seeking admission to the convent when she was a young girl.

As she sat at the bedside of her fevered husband she believed she heard a voice whisper: "He dies because God wishes to punish you!"

She clung to the sick man and begged God to impose another penance, and Monsieur Le Gras recovered. However, he died two years later, in 1625.

The young widow came to Monsieur Vincent and asked him to direct her fearful, troubled soul. She asked him to send her to a convent, but he bade her remain in her luxurious home in Paris and in order to banish the fear that was in her heart, to go to the sick and to the poor in the hospitals and in their hovels and do all the good she could for them.

After an adequate testing, Monsieur Vincent sent Mademoiselle Le Gras, for she was wealthy, to all the places where the priests of the mission congregation had labored in the rural districts, to establish Conferences of Charity. She was to travel as Monsieur Vincent's representative, counsel the newly organized conferences, supply them with alms, consult with the members, do all she deemed advisable to promote the work of Christian love of neighbor. For three years, despite her physical weakness and a constant threat to her health, she journeyed through France, in all sorts of weather, amid all the misery of the times and the perils of war. And she recovered health of body and of soul.

Then, having returned to Paris to spend the winter, she saw how the Conferences of Charity in the capital were in sore need of more members. She went to Monsieur Vincent and suggested that she take into her home young women from the country and establish a School of Charity in which these daughters of the peasants would be trained to be genuine Servants of Charity for work in the hospitals and in the homes of the poor.

Monsieur Vincent hesitated, for he always gave long, patient thought to important matters, and Mademoiselle Le Gras was obliged to wait.

Vincent himself had, on the occasion of the missions in rural parishes, learned to know more than one peasant maiden who did not wish to marry and would gladly devote her life to Christian charity. One of these was Marguerite Naseau, who lived near Suresnes. She tended her father's sheep, but in the loneliness of her shepherding she was seized by a vehement desire to learn to read and write. So she asked people who passed by to tell her one letter after the other, and soon the peasants of Suresnes were laughing at this strange shepherdess who craved to be learned.

When Monsieur Vincent came to Suresnes at the time of a mission, Marguerite learned of the Conferences of Charity, started at once for Paris and Saint-Lazare and told Vincent de Paul the great desire of her heart. He entrusted her to Mademoiselle Le Gras, who took the peasant girl into her splendid house.

Thus Marguerite Naseau became the first of the Servants of Charity who afterwards received from the people the appellation of honor, Sisters of Charity.

On the 29th of November, 1633, Monsieur Vincent placed four girls in charge of Mademoiselle Le Gras to be trained in her School of Charity, which she founded at this time, and also gave her the rule for the new congregation which was to unite these young peasant women in the sacred service of human suffering.

In this instance as in that of the Congregation of the Missions, Monsieur Vincent did not wish to establish a new religious order, but an entirely new society, for the old orders were bound to their monasteries and convents by their rules and the strict clausura, limited to the battle for self-perfection within the walls of their sacred houses. No previous founder had succeeded in breaking through the law of the cloister, the separation of the religious from the world.

Monsieur Vincent, of course, wished his new religious, like his mission priests, to live not in monasteries or convents, but in the world, wherever they might be sent. Therefore he once spoke as follows to the Daughters of Charity, as they were called at first, the Sisters of Charity, as they were called later, on the occasion of an instruction: "Let your convents be the houses of the poor; your cells, rented rooms; your chapel the parish church; your cloister the street.

And if you wish a clausura, let it be obedience. If you need a grille, let it be a loving fear of the Lord. And if you need a veil, let that be Christian modesty."

Vincent de Paul withstood Mademoiselle Le Gras's efforts to found a religious order. Only she, who was made superioress for life, did he permit to take perpetual vows. And though there were to be mother houses in which the members lived in common and mutually edified and strengthened each other, so that a constant stream of peasant girls would come and be trained in the School of Charity, they were not to remain in the house but to go to the hospitals.

Even in the wake of soldiers going out to the wars, Monsieur Vincent sent his Sisters of Charity. And when two of the four first ones fell ill and died in a few days' time, other girls volunteered at once upon receipt of the news, asking that they be sent into the war to do deeds of mercy.

So the Butterflies of God, as they were called, flitted from the house of Mother Louise de Marillac, their mother house, out into the world, and where they came upon the abode of sickness or misery, there they alighted. They filled the world with amazement at their deeds of mercy, so that one of the worst deniers of God and most intense haters of the Church the world has ever known, Voltaire, said of these Sisters of Charity: "Perhaps there is nothing more exalted and greater in the world than the sacrifice of beauty, youth and not seldom also noble birth, in order to assuage in the hospitals that mass of human misery the mere sight of which is so humiliating for our pride and so repugnant for our supersensitive feelings."

How truly these Sisters loved Christ was proved during the years of the French Revolution, when a stream of blood and puss burst from the body of the French people, but the Sisters allowed not even this hate, that tried to smash the Church, to keep them from doing heroic acts of mercy.

Unforgettable are the nuns who were dragged to the scaffold by an inhuman rabble in the month of June, 1794, at Cambrai, and who in the face of death in the midst of the howling throng began to chant: *"Salve, Regina . . . "* and whose thin, angelic voices sang above the heads of the bloodthirsty mob: *"Veni, Creator Spiritus . . .* Come, Holy Ghost, down upon this people and fill it with Thy works," until one voice after the other was stilled in death and at last one only sang, the youngest, till her head, too, fell beneath the axman's stroke.

Chapter XVII

LIKE A WOMAN HACKED TO PIECES

THERE are two elements mutually antagonistic whose true nature we do not discover until they appear together: the darkness of the night and the bright light of day. Only when the light has come forth from the darkness do we realize the gloom of night and the almost more than earthly radiance of the light.

Thus I see two kingdoms and the men who make them. In the days when Vincent de Paul walked the earth and stood close to the throne of France, often entered the apartments of the King and Queen to beg alms, there came into the same chambers the great ones of the world to advance their plans of empire. And these latter went forth again into the world to fill the land with deeds of horror. How close together are decay, with its sickly brilliance, and the birth of life and its pure waters!

At that time there sat on the French throne the thirteenth Louis, son of the fourth Henry, he of Navarre, and of Marie de Medici. He was a good ruler, strove after perfection and wished sincerely to be dissolved and enter into the kingdom of Heaven.

Beside him was his chancellor, Cardinal Richelieu,

truly one of the most powerful ones of the earth. His ambition was to make the kingdom of France, its glory and its power supreme among the nations, and the means which he employed to accomplish this brought unlimited woe upon the peoples of Europe and his own, the subjects of Louis XIII.

Richelieu saw that two powers stood opposed to his ambitious plans for the aggrandizement of France and her King.

The first of these forces he held to be the House of Austria and the Spain which was united with Austria and surrounded France. The power of the Hapsburgs extended from Austria to the Atlantic, and in those days the Netherlands belonged to Spain. To destroy this first opposing force, the cardinal-chancellor sent out his spies.

The second power which Richelieu held to imperil his plans was within France. This was the nobility, the eminent families with glorious traditions, who had through the centuries lived in their own domains and considered themselves equals of the King.

Monsieur Richelieu said to the nobles: All of France is a kingdom and the lands you hold are but royal fiefs. He wished to wipe out the old system of fiefs and reduce the nobles to the same level as the other subjects of the King, dependent on his favor.

Now the nobles strove against Richelieu's scheme, one conspiracy followed the other, civil wars blackened the land.

When the King of Spain was informed that Cardinal Richelieu was conducting secret negotiations in the Low Countries, to wrest them from Spain, and the further news came that Richelieu sought to deprive of his lands a brave but unstable and bombastic ruler, Charles IV, Duke of Lorraine, the Spanish King caused his troops to invade the Electorate of Treves, which was then under French protection.

In this way the flames of war were lighted. They burned unluckily for France and the enemy marched into King Louis's land.

Then came uprisings against Richelieu, in Paris and other cities, because the people believed he was losing the war.

The Spaniards did indeed cross into France from their Lowland possessions, and when the German cavalry general, Johann von Wörth, advanced across the Somme, his horsemen were within twenty hours' ride from Paris.

Thereupon the bells of Paris sounded the tocsin of war and there began the Thirty Years' War.

Monsieur Richelieu had schemed so that dissension among the Germans became his ally. He induced the Lutheran princes to war against the Catholic Emperor. Chief among these princes was the Duke of Saxe-Weimar, who came to Richelieu's assistance through Lorraine, together with the Swedish army.

In Paris, which seemed almost to be besieged by Johann von Wörth, the King caused an emergency army of thousands of men to be raised. All the men of the capital who were able to bear arms — mechanics and even the servants of the nobles — were recruited hurriedly into regiments and sent to Saint-Lazare, there to be drilled for military service.

Monsieur Vincent and his missionaries sought to maintain the religious routine of their lives amid the tumult of war plans, and when at dawn the drums beat and shouts of command broke the silence of the courtyards, Vincent knelt with his confreres in prayer for the peace of the nations. Then he summoned his priests, for the King of France had issued a decree that twenty of them should be chaplains in the new fighting force.

In the meantime the Duke of Saxe-Weimar had invaded Lorraine with his own and the Swedish troops, while the Duke of Lorraine tried to devastate the shores of the Rhine and the German cities situated there. And the fields were trampled by the hoofs of war horses.

When the King's emergency army of thirty thousand men set out from Paris to expel General von Wörth's cavalry, Monsieur Vincent's missionaries went along, and from the sacred tent that served as a chapel they ministered to the soldiers, by the priestly word in sermons, by the Sacrifice of the Mass and the Bread which is the Body of Christ, thus trying to make the recruits into soldiers who would keep their work of destruction within the bonds of humanity; trying to keep the army from becoming a beastly horde. The emergency force succeeded in driving the enemy from the land.

But then the plague struck at the French army, and the priests of Monsieur Vincent's society went at once to nurse the sick in the camps which the disease turned into places of foul corruption and death, until the plague subsided and in Paris the bells proclaimed victory. Then the populace thronged to see captured banners exhibited in the Church of Notre Dame and in a delirium of emotion it hailed Richelieu, whom it had so short a time before covered with maledictions.

Oh, you people reeling from the terror of threatened defeat into the wild enthusiasm of victory! How brief are the triumphs of an earthly kingdom and how fickle the fortunes of war! Victory and defeat succeed each other like alternating day and night.

What the hoofs of the war horses had not trampled, the foot soldiers had destroyed. Villages were heaps of fire-blackened ruins, and the peasants wandered about driving into the woods the few cattle left to them but being finally espied by a band of brutal soldiers and robbed of their last belongings.

Now the victors ravaged the land. In Lorraine the ruthless troops of Weimar's duke carried a banner on which was the image of a woman hacked to pieces and to her right and to her left stood soldiers with swords and firebrands. Under the image was an inscription saying that this was a picture of Lorraine. Thus the land was like a woman hacked to pieces.

The peasants fled to the forests, were hunted like wild animals by the soldiers, and slain. From the groves they peeked out to see their homes burning and they pressed their mouths close to the earth and bit off the grass and ground it between their teeth, for they had no other food.

From the cities and towns the people came into the forests to gather the acorns which in other times the peasants were wont to feed to their pigs. This was their bread.

Bells sounded hour after hour, day and night. Monasteries, convents sought by means of their bells to summon help, but succeeded only in luring constantly new bands of Soldateska, bent on plunder.

In the streets of the cities one saw even the daughters of nobles, shame surrendering to hunger, sneak among the houses to sell themselves to burghers for the sake of bread. The famine was so fierce that mothers murdered their children, to eat them, and children killed their mothers, to feed on their mothers' flesh. Like ghostly groups the hungry, demented ones trudged through the land, sought fortified places, there to enter in the hope of finding food. In the fields and along the highways one saw them in scattered heaps, the dying and the dead. At night the wolves of the forests came into the city streets and attacked the people still slinking there, for these beasts had become satiated with corpses and now desired living flesh.

Hungry people fell upon the bodies of the dead.

Then the plague assailed them and, poisoned by their horrible food, they died swiftly.

In those days priests of his society brought tidings of these horrors to Monsieur Vincent at Saint-Lazare, and he cried out in his anguish: "What do you say? It is a judgment on Lorraine, our enemy? And the Duke of Lorraine is arrayed against the French and therefore these things have come upon his people? Are not those poor wretches human beings, bound to us by a common faith in Jesus Christ? Do they not hunger as we do for the Bread of Life, are they not united with us in Christ when they suffer?"

At once he commanded his missionaries to reduce by one half the pittance of food and wine which he had allowed them, and dispatched one to Lorraine immediately. He took with him the food which had thus been saved.

Then Monsieur Vincent sped to the mother of the King of France, Anne of Austria; and to the Duchess d'Aiguillon, and he summoned the ladies of the Conferences of Charity and he sent them to the houses of the nobles and the rich, filling them with so much ardor by his description of the vast misery and desperate need in Lorraine that they gathered many alms and brought together all that they possibly could.

His missionaries he sent forth with all that was thus collected, sent them as messengers of help and hope, as physicians to combat the diseases of war in the towns of Lorraine.

For ten years Vincent de Paul carried on this work of charity, for scarcely did the war cease in one district than it flared up in another, always with a new and hellish rage.

One of his priests was sent by Monsieur Vincent on journeys of mercy thirty-five times during these ten years. The priest often carried huge sums, from twenty to thirty thousand livres, or more, hidden in his clothes; and in the disguise of a beggar he passed unharmed through the hordes of ruthless soldiery, played the fool, played all roles necessary to escape detection, until he reached one of the centers of suffering. There he changed himself into an angel of mercy and the blessing of Heaven was so plainly with him that not once in all his adventurous journeys did he lose a single sou of the sums he carried for the relief of dire want.

Wherever the misery was the worst, the mission priests established places of refuge, stations of help to which the hungry and the sick fled or crawled; and these when they had gained strength became assistants to Monsieur Vincent's envoys and in houses which had escaped destruction they set up asylums for the homeless, hospitals for the sick. Then they hurried to bury the dead, the victims of war's ferocity and horror.

But before they could complete the work of reconstruction, the forces of destruction came upon them in a new wave of cruelty.

The wretched victims tried to sneak through the

contingents of armed men and there began a vast flight, an exodus from Lorraine, and all of the refugees made Paris and the courtyards of Saint-Lazare their destination. A whole people sought refuge in the arms of one man of charity, Vincent de Paul.

He stood in the midst of the pitiable throng and called out to his aides, who were frightened by the onslaught of misery. Vincent admonished them and was kind to all. He sent his coworkers to divide the refugees into groups, seek shelters for them, place girls in the homes of sympathetic and generous families, so that they would have the necessities of life, a roof, food, clothing, until they could return to their country.

One who lived when these things took place tells us that so many fled from Lorraine that a century would be required to regain the loss in population.

One day there came to Monsieur Vincent, shy and embarrassed, a messenger with tidings of a new calamity. The nobles of Lorraine were suffering even more than had the people who found a refuge at Saint-Lazare. They had lost everything, no less than had the burghers, but their pride forbade them to show their need. So they kept up an appearance of wealth and died in solitary wretchedness. When he heard this, instead of being dumbfounded, Monsieur Vincent cried out, "O what joy you give me! Let us find new means of helping! Not one sou of what I have collected for the poor must be used for the nobles. For them we must tap new sources of help."

He hurried to the residence of the Count de Renty, who was known to be both rich and generous. To him he described the plight of the nobles of Lorraine and the two decided that a special organization should be formed, in such a way that the nobles of France would consider it an obligation of honor to assist the nobles of Lorraine. A list of the needy and shamed was compiled. In every city where Vincent's mission priests labored, they sought out those whose names were on this list.

The rich nobles whom Monsieur Vincent enlisted under the leadership of the Count de Renty met once a month at Saint-Lazare to ascertain how much would be needed to stay the want of the impoverished nobles for a month, and they never closed the meeting until the required sum had been subscribed by those present. Then they planned how their alms could be given in the most tactful manner. Many agreed to take the alms in person to those for whom they were intended and in doing so to ascertain their special needs and to convince them that they could accept the gifts of fraternal charity without loss of honor.

For eight years the organization continued this blessed work.

But always new forms of misery appeared in these terrible times. From England, from Scotland, from Ireland came exiles, priests and aristocrats, victims of the religious wars and the ruthless tyranny of Cromwell. For Cromwell, ruler of England, imprisoned Catholic nobles who opposed him and sold them like Negroes to plantations in America.

At the same time, a persecution of priests broke out in Italy. A price was put on the heads of priests to encourage betrayers and murderers, who harried the footsteps of these priests as they harried the English lords and Scottish lairds whom Cromwell persecuted.

The hunted ones fled through swamps, through forests, defenseless, often clad in nothing but rags, often torn to pieces by wolves before they could reach a place of refuge and of loving care established by Vincent and his missionaries.

Then in the extremity of need Monsieur Vincent went to ask audience of Cardinal Richelieu in the royal palace. The Chancellor's chambers were strictly guarded, at the King's command, because of threats against the Cardinal's life. But Vincent walked past the guards and found Richelieu at his desk, whence he sought to rule the destinies of the world.

Monsieur Vincent sank to his knees and implored the powerful statesman: "For God's sake, Monsieur Cardinal, make peace!"

They stood face to face, these two men: the proud one in whose heart there burned only one passion, the glory of the throne of France, its exaltation above all the thrones of Europe; and the servant of charity in the kingdom of Christ.

Through the lands their deeds marched, witnesses to the hearts from which they sprang.

And Cardinal Richelieu spoke: "You must understand, Monsieur Vincent, that I am laboring for the peace of the world and that I would establish it at once if it depended upon me alone. But how can a single man untie all the knots into which the nations have coiled themselves because of their passions?"

Wearily, Monsieur Vincent rose to his feet. Then Richelieu spoke to him: "When will you take for yourself the rest you ask me to give others?"

Vincent de Paul answered: "Our duties, Monsieur, know no end."

And he went forth to new deeds of compassion.

Chapter XVIII

PITY ON A DYING KING

CARDINAL RICHELIEU died in 1642. He had been unable to give peace to the world, nor had he succeeded in creating for the throne of France and its King the empire of which he had dreamed.

At a window of his palace sat the King, the thirteenth Louis, tired and pale. He gazed out over the roofs of Paris and beyond to the towers of Saint-Denis. Since Charlemagne's time, the Kings of France had been entombed there.

The thirteenth Louis felt in this hour how an unseen guest came into the room and laid its hand on his shoulder, as if admonishing him to arise and follow, as Monsieur Richelieu, the great Cardinal, had followed.

Louis nodded and said, "I am ready to go to Saint-Denis. Call Monsieur Vincent, he shall go with me."

One of the court servants hurried to Saint-Lazare to summon Vincent to stand by the King at his death. Vincent came and remained day after day for two weeks with the dying monarch, to wean his eyes from the futile things of this world. Once Louis XIII said, "Monsieur Vincent, if I recovered I would order all the Bishops of France to go to school to you at Saint-

Lazare for a time, so that after being instructed by you they would return to their bishoprics. God knows, I believe the people would then have peace."

But when the day came on which the physician appeared before him and said, "Majesty, it is my duty to tell you that you must prepare for the end," the King embraced him joyfully, saying: "I thank you for these good tidings! Call Monsieur Vincent, so he may take me in his arms."

And so it came to pass. Monsieur Vincent came and in his arms the thirteenth Louis fell asleep in death.

When all this had happened and the court's concern with the pomp of earthly mourning invaded the royal palace, Vincent left unobserved and at Saint-Lazare he and his missionaries prayed for the dead sovereign.

This was on the 14th of May, 1643, not an entire year after the death of Cardinal Richelieu.

The new King, the fourteenth Louis, was only four years old. The Queen Mother, Anne of Austria, was regent and in Richelieu's office was Monsieur Mazarin, an Italian by blood, of low origin, an upstart who had won a post close to the King by means of the Gondi way of the serpent. Without being a priest, he had managed to obtain the dignity of the cardinalate. He was the powerful successor of the great Richelieu and he ruled the land with exceptional deceit and trickery.

In order to increase his power, Mazarin made appointments according to favoritism, allowed himself to be bribed, sold benefices to those who agreed to divide the revenues with him, and made bishops and nobles dependent on him, creatures of his whims.

The Queen Mother, who could not escape the power of this man but feared for the safety of France, decided to place a council of conscience at the head of the State. The four members of this council were to watch all governmental actions. The first of the councilors was Monsieur Mazarin, the fourth Monsieur Vincent.

Cardinal Mazarin ruled the realm. All applications for offices or dignities were henceforth to be referred to the council of conscience and there voted on; and what Mazarin could not withhold from the council resulted in documents of all sorts being heaped upon Monsieur Vincent, petitions and inquiries in almost infinite numbers. The priest sought to be released from serving the council, but he was compelled to bear the burden for ten years.

Now Mazarin hated Vincent de Paul. He dared not, however, give vent to the secret raging hate excepting by an occasional word of mockery, as when he asked his haughty entourage whether they had noticed that a new patch had appeared on the priest's clothes in addition to the one previously the latest. "And see how tattered his girdle is!"

Nor was Vincent spared undeserved suspicions and false accusation, and one day the Queen called him into her presence, showed him a letter and asked, smilingly: "Well, Monsieur Vincent, what have you to say to this?"

Monsieur Vincent answered, "Oh, I know I am a great sinner."

And the Queen said, "But you must defend yourself."

He shook his head. "Of what was not our Lord Jesus Christ accused, and do we read that He defended Himself against false charges?"

The Queen of France nodded, sat in deep thought, then gave Vincent her hands. On whom else . . . ? On this man only, on no other could she depend.

Who was eager to acquire a bishopric? Who an abbey? Who a priory? Mazarin's system of favoritism had brought it about that even officers in the army were given high ecclesiastical dignities, so they could enjoy the revenues of benefices. At the court they laughed because a simple monk once wrote to his superior and addressed the letter to "My Most Reverend Lord Abbot, the Commander in the Field."

"Skimmers of the Church's goods," they were called, the favorites among whom the priests served like wage slaves.

So little was the seriousness of this situation appreciated that even so pious a king as the thirteenth Louis, who had died in the arms of Vincent de Paul, once gave the abbacy of Saint-Germain-des-Prés to a woman, the widow of the Duke of Lorraine, so she might meet her needs with its revenues.

Once Vincent said to a man avid after a prelacy benefice: "The angels fear to aspire to the dignity of a bishop, because the episcopal office is of such high grace and responsibility as to frighten even the angels. And you wish the Queen to make you a bishop for the sake of worldly goods which will enable you to live a carefree life in the spirit of the world!"

Constantly, persistently Monsieur Vincent endeavored to guard the purity of Church offices. Nor did he hesitate to imprison an abbess who deserved the punishment.

Meanwhile, beyond Paris war trampled the soil of France.

Chapter XIX

A Life Is Risked for Peace

ONCE again the kingdom of power in this world opposed the kingdom of our Lord Jesus Christ and His servant, Vincent de Paul.

It was the year 1648. Its money system shattered, the treasury of France was empty. To fill it again, the dictator of the realm, Cardinal Mazarin, decreed new taxes. Now France at that time had a Parliament and tax laws were not operative until this legislative body had approved the royal decree.

A storm of protest arose against Mazarin's new tax laws, and two parties were formed. One, composed of the Chancellor's adherents, was called the Mazarins; the other, made up of his opponents, called itself the Fronde. The latter gained the upper hand and soon the people marched in the streets of Paris singing songs that mocked Mazarin. Writings denouncing the mighty Cardinal were spread far and wide through the land.

When eager servants reported this to Mazarin, he laughed and said, "Let them keep on singing ballads at my expense, if only they pay my taxes!"

And he sent the police to the printing houses of

the Fronde and took possession of the leaflets which
attacked him, held him up to scorn. But he did not
destroy them, rather he brought them to Paris and
manipulated affairs so that the leaflets sold at high
prices. Then he boasted of the profit he had made
in this manner.

However, he caused two leaders of the Fronde to
be arrested and cast into prison. Scarcely had this
become known when the populace arose. Barricades
were erected in two hundred places and chains were
stretched across the streets; and the flag of the Fronde
floated above the barricades.

Then with the cries, "Long live the King!" and
"Down with Mazarin!" the mob appeared before the
royal palace and was joined by the triumphant Parliament in demanding of the Queen Mother the release
of the leaders whom Mazarin had imprisoned. At first
Anne of Austria, who was regent for the little King,
wished to withstand this demand. She was advised,
however, that the people were so rebellious that they
were ready to set fire to the palace and kill Mazarin,
and then she relented.

Among the rebels was Paul de Gondi, and at the
time he bore the title of coadjutor. He had been one
of Monsieur Vincent's pupils in the Gondi household
and was a nephew of the Archbishop of Paris, whom
he hoped to succeed in that high position.

The people withdrew in triumph with the two
liberated leaders and Paris celebrated this un-

precedented victory as a festival. That night the Queen Mother left Paris with the King, as did also Monsieur Mazarin, fleeing to Saint-Germain-en-Laye. That was the 6th of January in 1649.

But the next day the Parisians saw how a royal army surrounded the capital. The Prince de Conde was besieging the city with eight thousand men. The Parisians laughed. They numbered seven hundred thousand and had an army of their own of forty thousand men. The Coadjutor Paul de Gondi at his own expense raised a special regiment to break through the besiegers' circle. When this force passed through a city gate to do battle, the men, women, and children of Paris stood on the walls to witness the engagement. Fiddlers danced before the troops. Soon, however, the watchers saw how de Gondi's soldiers fell back when attacked by the intrepid followers of the Prince de Conde, and presently the whole regiment was fleeing back to safety within the city walls. And the fiddlers, throwing away violins and bows, fled with the regiment. The rout was comical, it seemed to the people, who clapped their hands with glee and good-naturedly awarded the crown of victory in this first encounter to the troops of the Conde.

There was nothing comical in what followed. The Parisians began to go about with long faces when they became aware that the Prince de Conde's small army not only prevented the peasants from bringing food into the city, but devastated the countryside and set fire to the villages. At night the grim flares lighted up the skies about Paris.

Then hunger entered the city, and the contest of the citizens began to be waged within the walls. The Fronde put a regiment of its troops in Saint-Lazare and as it was known that Monsieur Vincent took the Queen Mother's part and wished to arbitrate between the factions in this civil war, the leaders of the Fronde became angry, for they would tolerate none who was not their partisan. At night Vincent gathered his priests, filled them with courage. Then he went to his room, wrote a letter to the president of the Parliament, informing him that toward morning he would leave the city to visit the regent and beg that peace be made.

Monsieur Vincent risked his life when he passed through one of the city gates, dared the iron ring which the Conde had drawn around it, and braved the spring floods. Once he almost drowned, once the soldiers were about to kill him when a citizen of Clichy ran to his rescue. Every citizen of Clichy knew Monsieur Vincent.

When he reached Saint-Germain-en-Laye, the Queen Mother received him at once and conversed with him for more than an hour behind locked doors.

At once it was rumored at the court that Monsieur Vincent was with the regent, counseling her to dismiss Mazarin because that was the only way peace could be restored. The rumor reached the Cardinal, too. For a moment he paled, and was standing in deep thought

on how to ward off this danger when a servant announced that Vincent de Paul was in an anteroom,
waiting to deliver a message from the Queen.

How often had the powerful Cardinal, in his
impotent rage, mocked this simple priest! Now the
humble man came at the behest of the regent of the
realm, came as an agent of fate. For a long time the
two remained in secret conference, and when Monsieur Vincent emerged from the room it was to return
to the Queen. However, that evening he left Saint-
Germain-en-Laye crestfallen. He had been defeated
in the duel.

Nor could Vincent return to Paris. He knew full
well that his mission priests at Saint-Lazare were
threatened with many evils, which they might the
more successfully ward off if he were not among
them. So he managed to reach a little manor, beyond
the besiegers' circle and secluded.

It was a cruel winter. The peasants whose huts had
been burned down by the Conde's troops, raged
plundering through the hamlets. The manor, when
Vincent reached it, he found already looted and the
servants could offer him nothing but poor bread. And
they suffered intensely from the cold, because wood
was wanting. The roaming, homeless ones whom Monsieur Vincent wished to help increased daily in
number.

So Vincent fled farther, to Marseilles.

But in Paris, where even the monastery of Saint-

Lazare had been besieged by the Fronde's adherents, two thousand beggars gathered day after day to receive the soup, *panade,* the one-dish meal which Monsieur Vincent had promised them.

Summer came. Monsieur Vincent, returning from Marseilles to Paris, fell sick in a miserable village. For many years he had been unable to travel on foot, because of the leg wounds received when he served as a galley slave. He was compelled to ride. Plagued by a fever constantly, a fierce stream of pain shot through the body and concentrated in his wounded legs, causing him to suffer so excruciatingly that he lost consciousness.

When this came upon him, he would even in the heat of summer have his body covered with heavy quilts and steaming water in pewter tubs placed close to his bed. This intensified the pain immensely, but he endured it for hours. Then the fever would vanish.

The news of Monsieur Vincent's plight reached even Paris and the Duchess d'Aiguillon. She had, three years before, presented Vincent with a carriage and two horses, because of his wounded legs, but he had not accepted the gifts and the carriage and horses had remained in the stable. The Duchess would not take them back. Now in his extremity Vincent was forced to bow to the kindness of the Duchess and he was brought to Paris in the coach. He found the city decorated for an intoxicating feast, for Paris had capitulated. The young King had returned to his palace, and in a frenzy of joy, as though no greater happiness had ever come to them, the people shouted in the streets:

"Vive de Conde!" — who had defeated them.

"Vive Mazarin!" — whom they had cursed.

The month was June, the year 1649.

Chapter XX

I Send You Forth to Save Lives

THE peace did not last long.

One evening as the Prince de Conde was crossing a bridge that spanned the Seine, there was a sudden tumult behind him, and a shot rang out.

Later it became known that hired assassins had made an unsuccessful attempt on the Prince's life. Spies of Cardinal Mazarin had interfered and fallen upon the would-be murderers in the moment they had chosen for their dastardly deed.

The wildest of rumors whirled through Paris. It was said the shot at the Prince had been fired from within the ranks of the Fronde. Others whispered that Mazarin himself had instigated the attack and also the frustration of it. The whole affair, some contended, had been a droll plot to deceive the Conde and to cause his downfall.

In the Parliament there were violent scenes between the partisans of the Prince de Conde and those of Paul de Gondi, for the former accused the Coadjutor of having fathered the attempt to murder him.

The two old factions attacked each other, but quite suddenly it became clear that the Fronde and their leader, de Gondi, were on the side of Mazarin. The Prince de Conde was arrested and cast into prison.

This was the signal for a new civil war. The followers of the imprisoned prince rose in all parts of the land, did not shrink from allying themselves with the Spaniards, the enemies of their King.

In those days a priest of his mission society came back to Monsieur Vincent and Saint-Lazare from a trip to Italy and reported misery full of horror, such as human eyes had never seen, in the place called Rethel.

Two thousand Spanish corpses lay on the battle-field, no hand had been raised to bury them. They had been there for eight weeks, exposed to the ravages of wild beasts, wolves and buzzards, which fed upon them. The foulness arising from these thousands of unburied bodies had caused the plague to break out. One disease followed quickly in the wake of another among the people, who did not know why this was happening.

Then Monsieur Vincent at once sent a new contingent of his priests to Rethel, to bury the two thousand Spanish corpses and bring help to the innumerable sick.

Scarcely had this been attended to when a second tidings of misery arrived. There were in those days many exiled and fugitive Irishmen in France. They constituted regiments of their own to fight for the King of the land in which they were guests. But when winter came these Irish troops were sent into quarters at Troyes and they took their wives and their children with them. They lacked even the necessities of life, marched in rags, looked far more like a band of beggars than a regiment of soldiers. Nobody concerned himself about these Irishmen and their families. So they haunted the streets and alleys of Troyes, the men, women, and children, shelterless, not knowing whence food would come to them. They ate what was thrown from the houses to the dogs but the animals refused to eat.

When the sufferings of these people was made known to him, Monsieur Vincent sent his coworkers to Troyes with clothing and food, with instructions to find quarters for the soldiers, gather the sick into a hospital, care for the children, bring consolation to all of them in their piteous plight.

In that year also, the retreating army of the French King, lacking utterly all it ought to have had, was attacked at Guide. The soldiers collapsed in the streets, were too weak to arise and march on. Far across the land the retreat of this miserable army could be traced by the dead and the dying that marked its route.

The fields of corn had long since been plundered by roving hordes, in the homes of the villagers there was no longer any food, the people of the cities had been robbed of everything. People lay on the ground to bite off blades of grass. They crawled in the meadows like grazing animals, no longer having strength enough to rise up. They dragged themselves to trees and gnawed at the bark, tore with their teeth the rags that partly clothed them. Some hacked off their own hands and feet and tore the flesh from the bones, as dogs do.

Wherever these things took place, there mission priests of Monsieur Vincent soon appeared, and the Daughters of Charity, the Sisters, to save what could be saved. "The soldiers march through the lands to kill," said Vincent to them at this time. "You I send forth to help, to save lives."

The rebels won the upper hand, compelled the Queen Mother to liberate the Conde and send Mazarin into banishment. Mazarin went to Metz, but retained the reins of government in his hands, prepared to return when his hour struck.

The Prince de Conde, scarcely out of prison, returned to the Parliament, and soon new, fierce conflicts took place between his party and that of the Coadjutor de Gondi. This time the passions raged so bitterly that adherents of the Prince sought to throw themselves upon de Gondi and stab him to death.

But the Coadjutor wrested the poinard from the man who tried to kill him.

"I would I might strangle you with my hands!" shouted this partisan of the prince.

De Gondi said: "I believe you, but not for that reason we shall fight like men. I am a priest and you are a coward."

To such heights had the hate between the factions mounted.

The battle in the Parliament waged for hours. The Queen threw her influence to the Coadjutor de Gondi, the Prince de Conde left Paris again to raise new levies, and civil war engulfed the country once more.

Mazarin returned from Metz and devastation that seemed boundless swept over the land.

Wherever the armies came, the peasants, where any of them still lived, having escaped earlier attacks, took the last cattle they had and fled, until overtaken by one of the roving bands of freebooters.

Messengers returning to Monsieur Vincent told him of the distress in a place called Etamps. And when the priests of the Congregation of the Missions and the Sisters of Charity he sent out arrived there, they saw on both sides of the city gates a huge pile of corpses, soldiers of the Queen slain by the foe. The gate was open and the city as if dead. When the priests entered through the gate, the spectacle of immense piles of dead bodies was repeated. But these corpses were of soldiers in the army of the Prince of Conde. The corpses lay among stinking dunghills. And amid these bodies and the rotting carcasses of slaughtered horses they found the bodies of women and children.

Only a few persons wandered, like ghosts, in the streets; like skeletons, and in their eyes the fire of fever glowed like fitful torches.

The aides of Vincent de Paul set to work burying the dead, cleansing the houses, collecting the sick in a hospital, succoring the beggars, as they had in so many other places.

And thus they did as they went from city to city, village to village. To Juvisy, a suburb of Paris, Monsieur Vincent sent a wagonload of food day after day, and a bagful of money. This he continued to do for many weeks, as also for the sufferers at Atys and many other places.

Vincent's workers knew no hesitation whatsoever in going to the houses of the rich to beg for alms. They collected all anyone gave them, uninterruptedly — food, clothes, money, for distribution among the victims of all the horrors that war inflicts upon a people.

Then Monsieur Vincent hastened to the Queen, the regent, and to Mazarin; then he broke through the wild horde of soldiers, to the tent of the Prince de Conde; then back to the Cardinal-Chancellor, then to the Coadjutor de Gondi, once more to the Queen-Regent — and finally there was peace again.

But those in power did not make a peace such as Monsieur Vincent desired. After concluding peace they looked about for the guilty ones and the while they pledged peace they began anew to harass each other.

It was the 16th of December, 1652, when Monsieur Vincent was informed that Cardinal Mazarin had become reconciled with the Conde, but had caused Paul de Gondi to be arrested and thrown into prison.

The Coadjutor lay in chains a number of years. And Monsieur Vincent, who did not cease to send his priests and Sisters through the land to heal the wounds which the barbarous civil war had inflicted upon the people, often thought prayerfully of the wayward Paul de Gondi and implored Heaven to grant him peace in God, not the peace of the world, which is really nothing but war wearing a mask.

Paul de Gondi was still in prison when his uncle, the Archbishop of Paris, died. From his cell and his chains he put forward his claim to the high office. He was Archbishop of Paris in later years; was such while still in prison. And when he was set free and sat in the great episcopal chair of the French capital, he shuddered and there was given him the grace of conversion.

Chapter XXI

FATHER OF THE FOUNDLINGS

OF THE multitude of good deeds for which countless human hearts have blessed him, one more than any other brought Monsieur Vincent the love of the people. And of this I will now tell.

Paris was at that time a city into which streamed a vast number of people, seeking shelter within its walls. The houses had to be built a number of stories high, every foot of ground was used, and it was said that Paris was several cities built one on top of the other. The streets were narrow and as full of holes as the roads in the villages beyond the capital.

At night, when darkness lay upon the city, only such as feared the light were abroad. All who could keep away from the alleys did so, not only because they had to be accompanied by servants to light the way with torches and lanterns, but also because armed guards were needed to ward off the attacks of robbers.

A royal decree provided that in winter all theatrical performances begin at two o'clock in the afternoon and end by five o'clock, so that the citizens who were devoted to the theater could return home unmolested before darkness settled over Paris.

Of the manifold crimes committed under the cover of night, one of the most revolting was undoubtedly this, that mothers, either because of poverty or moral degradation, were wont to rid themselves of their little children by taking them stealthily to the Church of Notre Dame and laying them bundled on the church steps.

The King's watchmen, whose duty it was to keep the night roamers within bounds, were instructed to bring all the infants abandoned at Notre Dame to the port of Saint-Landry, to a house there that was dismal and called by the people *La Couche;* that is, the crib or cradle.

In this dismal house lived a widow and her two servants, and to them all the foundlings were delivered. A report on each baby was made by the police and the widow received a small compensation from the State for the care of each child. But because each year the abandoned infants numbered three or four hundred and the money the widow received was not enough to provide proper care for all of them, *La Couche* became a place of misery. The weeping of the neglected babies sounded in its rooms. In all corners, even on the floors they lay, hungry, unwashed. The widow and her servants could not do all the work necessary, so they often resorted to the use of a potion which caused the infants to sleep for a long time. But the poisonous nature of the potion often proved fatal, the eyes of the little ones became glazed, the tender human blossoms wilted.

And it was known in Paris that anyone who wished to adopt a foundling might purchase one for a few pennies at the dismal house in Saint-Landry. So beggars came to *La Couche* and bought babies, made them cripples, gouged out their eyes, rendered them objects of compassion, so that when clothed in rags and carried in the streets as their own, they would stir the pity of the rich and cause a stream of alms to flow into the pockets of the beggars.

Thus out of greediness they multiplied the suffering of the babies abandoned by their mothers. Nor did they hesitate to maltreat the helpless little creatures so brutally that many of them died in a few hours. Then the merciless beggars would throw the tiny bodies aside and go to Saint-Landry in search of more victims.

There were in those days some persons so obsessed by superstition that they believed certain concoctions would unfailingly cure human sickness if the ingredients included the blood of innocent children or pieces of a child's heart. Some went so far as to maintain that the coming of old age and of death itself could be prevented and that the old could rejuvenate themselves by bathing in the blood of children.

Much talk there was in Paris concerning the sinister house at Saint-Landry. The talk penetrated even to the court of the King, was whispered in the houses of the rich and of the nobles no less than in the homes of the common people. But no one was found who did

anything to change matters until Monsieur Vincent, in
the year 1638, came to Mademoiselle Le Gras, the
Mother Superior of his Sisters of Charity, and bade her
send a number of Sisters to the dismal house, to see
for themselves what the conditions were and then
report to him.

Quickly the investigators returned to tell Monsieur
Vincent what they had seen and heard. They were
overwhelmed by pity and distress. They could scarcely
tell him all they had experienced, so much were they
shaken by the sights and sounds of Saint-Landry's
place of pain and horror.

"The infants whom Herod slaughtered met a kindly,
an enviable fate, compared to the fate of the little ones
at Saint-Landry," they told Vincent.

Now the priest appointed an hour at which a number of ladies were to meet with Mademoiselle Le Gras.
To them he told of the foundlings' misery, and the
Sisters who had gone there were present to corroborate
all he said.

What was to be done? They would have liked most
of all to take entire charge of the dismal house, but
they did not have the means with which to do this.

And Monsieur Vincent advised that, far from returning to *La Couche* and leaving the infants there,
they ought to rescue as many as possible by having
them taken care of by the women who were at the
meeting. They decided at once to take twelve of the
little ones, chosen by lot, and bring them from Saint-

Landry to a house in the Rue des Boulangers and establish a foundlings' refuge there.

Goats were obtained, later a cow, and a number of Sisters of Charity mothered the abandoned babies.

As the alms which they collected increased, they were able to take a steadily increasing number of children into their center of love and tender care.

However, in the course of the years war plunged the land into such wretchedness that it became more and more difficult to secure sufficient means for this, one only among so many deeds of mercy. The times were so hard that the Sisters knew not how they would manage to feed the infants and rear them until they were grown old enough to take care of themselves. Sometimes the Sisters, for all the ardor they had for this work entrusted to them by Monsieur Vincent, found it almost impossible to obtain even enough of the plainest food for their little charges.

But behold, once again they succeeded in doing what seemed impossible!

It was said that Vincent de Paul often trudged through the alleys of the worst quarters of Paris on winter nights, to seek out and bring to the Rue des Boulangers refuge the tiny babes abandoned by their mothers. O God, how quickly the house was filled! And when at night Mademoiselle Le Gras heard a knocking at the door — and she knew this knocking apart from all others — and opened it and saw Monsieur Vincent standing there with a poor little one in his wide mantle, what was she to do? Each new guest threatened the lives of those already there. And yet, how could her tender motherly heart commit the crime of refusing to try, at least, to save this newcomer too?

Once, so they said, when Monsieur Vincent was hurrying along a dark alley, he was set upon by highwaymen. They held him fast and threatened to kill him if he did not give them his purse.

"See, I have nothing," Vincent is said to have told them, "excepting this infant," and he pushed back his mantle and showed them the foundling. "But come to Saint-Lazare and I will give you what I have."

The robbers recognized, then, that this was Monsieur Vincent. They fell upon their knees and begged him for his blessing. They believed that nothing more precious than that could be taken from him. And he blessed them and continued safely through the alleys and back to the Rue des Boulangers.

In the year 1648 the misery had increased to such tremendous proportions, because of the incessant wars and the unrest and revolts in Paris itself, that the Servants of Charity feared they had finally come to the end of their resources, did not know how they could possibly continue to shelter and feed the little ones. But Monsieur Vincent summoned all to help them, called noble ladies, duchesses and countesses, rich citizens' wives, and men, too, to gather at the home of the Duchess d'Aiguillon, who had often come to his assistance, and helped him in his work for the galley slaves.

He had estimated that to care for all the children now in the house in the Rue des Boulangers for the remainder of the year would require forty thousand livres.

And there was also the matter of space. The foundlings' refuge was now filled beyond its usual capacity. Many of the little ones had to be sent to villages near by, there to be cared for by peasant women, and Sisters of Charity had been engaged in visiting the children thus placed; or a Brother designated by Monsieur Vincent traveled about visiting the foster mothers and the babies entrusted to them. But in these terrible times, when armed groups roved about, driving the people out of villages, burning huts so that the peasants fled to the forests, some returning later only to be driven forth again by another band — in such times it was well-nigh impossible to supervise this phase of the work properly.

Monsieur Vincent had gone to Queen Anne and begged her to help him, and she had assured him a yearly subsidy of twelve thousand livres. But twenty-eight thousand more livres were needed, and where would they come from? It was possible, he told his co-workers, that the Queen Mother would also place the castle of Bicetre, out in the country, at their disposal for the foundlings, but it was doubtful whether the castle could be used permanently, because it was situated in a marshy district and was therefore not suitable as a living place for the delicate infants.

The ladies who had assembled at Vincent's bidding were utterly discouraged. It seemed to them that they would, this time, be compelled to surrender, to abandon the work. But Monsieur Vincent arose and spoke, "Very well, my dear ladies! You took these tiny creatures out of compassion, after their natural mothers had abandoned them. Now consider well whether you will desert them. Will you cease to be the mothers of these children and become their judges? Their lives are in your hands. It is time to render the verdict, so we may know whether no more love is to be given them. If you continue to devote yourself to these babes in charity, they will live; but they will surely die if you forsake them now. Our experience does not permit us to doubt that this is true."

This had so much of harshness, of irrevocable finality that all who heard the words kept them in their memories and they have been transmitted verbatim. All were stirred to the depths of their souls, and when Monsieur Vincent raised his hand as a signal for the momentous decision, all the ladies broke into tears. Many of them took what they wore of rings, necklaces, and other jewelry and shoved them across the table to Vincent. They embraced each other weeping and there was not one who was not resolved to carry on, placing the fate of the work in God's care.

Monsieur Vincent saw to it that the Castle Bicetre was placed by the Queen at the disposal of the foundlings and those who cared for them. Some of the infants were given into the custody of foster mothers.

However, what Vincent had feared came to pass: the castle proved unhealthy, because of its location, and the children had to be brought back to Paris. A second house was secured in the Saint-Lazare quarter, and there the foundlings were mothered by the Sisters of Charity until they were old enough to take care of themselves.

Chapter XXII

THE BLESSINGS OF A DYING MAN

WHEN I consider the multitude of the good deeds of Monsieur Vincent, it seems to me that I stand in the midst of the Alps and am gazing about. As far as the eye can see, the army of peaks lies spread out, even to the distant horizon. Only the mountains which are nearest to me do I see wholly and clearly. And the more I try to survey the entire range, the less distinctly do I see the single peaks. Then I am rapt in wonder at the vastness of the mountains lying at my feet, my gaze is lost in their majesty and their numbers, and if I raise my eyes to look into the distance, I am overwhelmed by the knowledge that I might travel many thousands of miles and would not even then come to the end of these mountains of good deeds.

At first I saw Monsieur Vincent journeying on foot, from place to place — but then I saw how he grew lame, for the chains of a galley slave had lacerated his feet. They tried to bind him to the earth, tried to stop him from journeying.

Then I saw Monsieur Vincent mount a horse and ride farther along the highway of his compassionate deeds.

But the wounds of his legs seemed like wounds inflicted by Hell, and I saw him overcome by fever as
he rode through the land, and the general of the
army of good deeds lay prostrate on the battlefield of
this world. I saw how he forced himself to arise, how
he reeled, how from Paris the kindly souled Duchess
d'Aiguillon sent horses and coach to transport the
stricken commander. However, there came the hour in
which even in a carriage he must needs have someone
to lean upon. Since the year 1658 he had not been able
to leave Saint-Lazare.

More and more he was driven into the corner by
the insidious malady. Soon he could no longer descend
the stairs to the sacristy, and when he came to the
altar to read Mass, his assistants had the sacred vestments placed there in readiness for him. When Monsieur Vincent noticed this for the first time, he stood
for a moment in helpless astonishment. Then he
smiled. "Now I have become a great lord," said he,
"now I am like a Bishop, for whom the vestments are
placed on the altar."

Soon he could no longer descend to the chapel. His
priests of the Congregation of the Missions arranged
a little chapel in a room next to his cell and to this
he let himself be carried, in a chair.

In August of the year 1660 this occurred for the
first time. He had for some time been unable to
offer up the Holy Sacrifice, could only receive Holy
Communion. He was 79 years old.

In those days one of the young priests of the missions in the house of Saint-Lazare wrote a letter and in it reported that in his opinion Monsieur Vincent had only a few days to live. Then he wrote of other matters and forgot what he had written concerning the old priest. When the letter was finished he went, as was customary, to Vincent's room to have him read the letter.

Thus Vincent de Paul learned how critical his condition was, through the carelessness of one his young associates.

When Vincent came to that part of the letter which referred to his condition, he paused a moment, looked up at the writer, who now realized what he had done and was thoroughly discomfited, but Monsieur Vincent smiled at him and said, kindly, "I thank you for the gentle admonition you have given me. You believe that a man in my condition ought not to concern himself so much about the world, but turn his thoughts to the last things. But so that you may not be disedified, because I continue to concern myself about my missionaries and the Sisters of Charity and all of their works in the world, I will tell you that I have for the past eighteen years secretly prepared myself each night for the hour that is now so near."

In this way it was revealed that Vincent de Paul, who had been tormented by a fever probably an entire half of his life, had long ago expected death.

Early in the morning of the 26th of September,

1660, he let himself be dressed, for he could no longer put on his clothes unassisted, and two Brothers carried him in a chair to the near-by chapel, so he could be present during the celebration of Mass.

When they brought him back to his room, he fell into a faint. He clung to the chair and they could not put him to bed. He moaned with pain. One of the Brothers ran at once to call a physician.

After some hours Monsieur Vincent awoke from the fainting spell and said smilingly to the physician standing beside him, "The sister is coming to visit her brother." (He meant that Sister Death was coming after Brother Sleep.)

One of his priests bent over him and bade him remember his last confession of sins before God, and began to recite the Confiteor aloud.

Vincent joined in the prayer. But his voice grew weaker and weaker and finally he sank into another spell of faintness.

The priest who was preparing him for death whispered to him to give his thought to God in this last hour, and from out of his faintness Vincent spoke: "Yes — yes — yes!"

His spiritual sons came and asked for his blessing.

His weak voice said he did not deem himself worthy to bless them, but to console them he would do so.

Would he not bless his priests of the Congregation of the Missions?

"Yes!"

— the Sisters of Charity?

"Yes!"

— the beggars and the poor?

"Yes!"

— the pitiable foundlings?

"Yes!"

— the Queen Mother and King Louis?

"Yes!"

— Monsieur Mazarin?

And once more all of them passed before him in spirit, all whom he had known since his childhood: his father — his mother — his brothers and sisters — the judge from Sore — Marguerite of Valois — the fourth Henry — the thirteenth Louis, who had died in his arms — Paul de Gondi — the Count and the Countess de Gondi — Mademoiselle Le Gras — the Duchess d'Aiguillon — the friends of Chatillon and those of Clichy — all, all of them — the slaves of the galleys and the numberless victims of misery in Lorraine, Picardy, and Gascony.

Again and again he fainted away. And always new visitors came, stirred him out of his sleep.

"Do not sleep! Do not sleep!"

To sleep was to sink into death. "Do not sleep, Father — Father, bless us!"

And so again and again he raised his hand in blessing.

Thus he sat in the chair from the morning of the 26th of September, throughout the day, through the evening, into the night, alternately fainting away and awakening to give his blessing, until he died early the next morning, toward half past four o'clock.

It was the 27th of September, in the year of our Lord 1660.

Nihil obstat: H. B. Ries, Censor librorum
Imprimatur: ✠ Samuel A. Stritch, Archiepiscopus Milwaukiensis
December 23, 1938